Book G

Specific Skill Series

Identifying Inferences

William H. Wittenberg

Fifth Edition

D1194862

SRA/McGraw-Hill

Columbus, Ohio

SRA/McGraw-Hill

*A Division of The **McGraw·Hill** Companies*

Printed in the United States of America.

Send all inquiries to:
    SRA/McGraw-Hill
    8787 Orion Place
    Columbus, OH 43240-4027

ISBN 0-02-688007-5

        4 5 6 IPC 02 01 00

PURPOSE:

IDENTIFYING INFERENCES is designed to develop one of the most difficult interpretive skills—arriving at a *probable* conclusion from a limited amount of information. IDENTIFYING INFERENCES requires the readers to *read between the lines*. They must utilize previously acquired knowledge and past experiences in order to fully comprehend the message of the text.

FOR WHOM:

The skill of IDENTIFYING INFERENCES is developed through a series of books spanning ten levels (Picture, Preparatory, A, B, C, D, E, F, G, H). The Picture Level is for pupils who have not acquired a basic sight vocabulary. The Preparatory Level is for pupils who have a basic sight vocabulary but are not yet ready for the first-grade-level book. Books A through H are appropriate for pupils who can read on levels one through eight, respectively. **The use of the *Specific Skill Series Placement Test* is recommended to determine the appropriate level.**

THE NEW EDITION:

The fifth edition of the *Specific Skill Series* maintains the quality and focus that has distinguished this program for more than 25 years. A key element central to the program's success has been the unique nature of the reading selections. Nonfiction pieces about current topics have been designed to stimulate the interest of students, motivating them to use the comprehension strategies they have learned to further their reading. To keep this important aspect of the program intact, a percentage of the reading selections have been replaced in order to ensure the continued relevance of the subject material.

In addition, a significant percentage of the artwork in the program has been replaced to give the books a contemporary look. The cover photographs are designed to appeal to readers of all ages.

SESSIONS:

Short practice sessions are the most effective. It is desirable to have a practice session every day or every other day, using a few units each session.

SCORING:

Pupils should record their answers on the reproducible worksheets. The worksheets make scoring easier and provide uniform records of the pupils' work. Using worksheets also avoids consuming the exercise books.

It is important for pupils to know how well they are doing. For this reason, units should be scored as soon as they have been completed. Then a discussion can be held in which pupils justify their choices. (The Integrated Language Activities, many of which are open-ended, do not lend themselves to an objective score; thus there are no answer keys for these pages.)

GENERAL INFORMATION ON *IDENTIFYING INFERENCES*:

The difference between a *conclusion* and an *inference*, as presented in this series, is that a conclusion is a logical deduction based upon conclusive evidence, while an inference is an "educated guess" based upon evidence that is less than conclusive. Read this sample:

> Captain Fujihara quickly parked the fire truck, grabbed his helmet, and rushed into the house at 615 Oak Street.

You can *conclude* that Captain Fujihara knows how to drive because that ability was required to park the fire truck. You can *infer* that there is a fire at 615 Oak Street because Captain Fujihara took his helmet and rushed into that house. This is an inference because firefighters do rush to put out fires. It is an inference because there may be another reason for the firefighter's rushing to the house. Captain Fujihara may live there and be late for supper. Thus an inference is supported by evidence, but the evidence is not necessarily conclusive.

SUGGESTED STEPS:
1. Pupils read the text. On levels C-H, after reading, pupils examine the statements that follow the text to determine whether each is a factually true statement (T), a false statement (F), or a valid inference (I). ("True" statements are those about which the reader can be *certain* from the text.) On lower levels, pupils determine which statement about the text or picture is probably true.
2. Then pupils reexamine the text or picture for evidence to support their decisions.
3. Pupils record their answers on the worksheets.

RELATED MATERIALS:
Specific Skill Series Placement Tests, which enable the teacher to place pupils at their appropriate levels in each skill, are available for the Elementary (Pre-1–6) and Midway (4–8) grade levels.

About This Book

In a story, a writer does not tell the reader everything. A careful reader is able to make educated guesses about things the author does not tell. An educated guess is a guess that is based on facts the author provides plus the reader's own knowledge and experience. For example, an author may write the following in a story:

Harry clutched a handkerchief tightly in his fingers. Sobbing, he raised his hand to wipe away the tears that trickled down his cheeks.

You can make an educated guess that Harry is sad, based on the fact that he is crying and on your own knowledge that people sometimes cry when they are sad.

This kind of educated guess is called an **inference**. You cannot be *certain* that your inference is correct. In the example above, Harry may be crying because he has hurt himself. Or he may be crying because he is very happy. Other details in the story will help you make the best possible guess.

In this book, you will read short stories. Then you will read four sentences about each story. You will have to decide whether each sentence is true (T), false (F), or an inference (I). A true statement tells a fact from the story. A false statement is one that is not true. An inference says something that is *probably* true based on facts in the story and your own knowledge and experience. More than one sentence about one story may be true, false, or an inference. You must read each sentence carefully to decide which it is.

1.   Dust swirled from beneath the churning wheels and rose in an angry cloud above the truck. Finding it hard to breathe, Sergeant Anderson closed the windows. He felt bad for the soldiers riding in the open back. How could they breathe at all! It had been hours since they had left their base, hours since they had seen any sign of life, hours since they had had any water. Anderson glanced quickly at the swooping and soaring vultures following overhead. The birds seemed to sense the soldiers' helplessness. What an omen! Sergeant Anderson felt very nervous.

---

2.   Once upon a time, a wolf lay on the ground, recovering from an injury. He saw a sheep passing by and cried out to her, "Good stranger, would you bring me some water? I could probably get some meat for myself, if only I could have some water!"

    The sheep pondered, then replied, "I will not, for I can see that if I brought you the water, you would have *no* trouble getting the meat!"

---

3.   Ms. Jackson's voice shook a little as she gave the students their assignment for the period. She wasn't used to teaching seventh and eighth graders. Most of the time she worked with younger students, and this group of teenagers made her a little nervous. They looked so grown-up, and the work they were doing was quite advanced. But she knew Mr. Andrews well. "What he would do, I'll do," she thought.

---

4.   Willard had lived his entire life by the sea, having learned at his father's knee the art of sailing. Now, many years later, he was setting out on the ultimate challenge—to sail solo around the world. This voyage would provide the maximum test for Willard. The difficult task of single-handed sailing, coupled with months of solitude, would bring many experienced sailors to their breaking point. But Willard was determined not to be found among those victims.

---

5.   Thomas Alva Edison watched in expectation as his assistant, Charles Bachelor, removed the mold from the furnace. Within was the priceless filament that Edison hoped would climax his experiments. As Bachelor removed the filament, it broke. "Let's try again," Edison said. Not until three days later was an intact filament successfully mounted inside a glass bulb. Quickly the air inside the bulb was exhausted and the current turned on. The filament glowed brightly! Disregarding their seventy-four sleepless hours, the two experimenters watched the first electric light burn for forty more hours.

UNIT 1

			T	F	I
1.	(A)	Clouds of dust made breathing difficult.	☐	☐	☐
	(B)	The sergeant feared that they might not return safely from the mission.	☐	☐	☐
	(C)	Beautiful green trees lined the sides of the roadway.	☐	☐	☐
	(D)	Sergeant Anderson opened the windows of the truck.	☐	☐	☐

			T	F	I
2.	(A)	The sheep concluded that the wolf planned to eat her.	☐	☐	☐
	(B)	The sheep thought about the wolf's request.	☐	☐	☐
	(C)	The wolf was taking a nap.	☐	☐	☐
	(D)	The sheep and the wolf knew each other.	☐	☐	☐

			T	F	I
3.	(A)	Ms. Jackson was substituting as a teacher for Mr. Andrews.	☐	☐	☐
	(B)	Ms. Jackson's voice shook a little.	☐	☐	☐
	(C)	Most of the time Ms. Jackson taught high school.	☐	☐	☐
	(D)	The work the students were doing was quite advanced.	☐	☐	☐

			T	F	I
4.	(A)	Sailing was a new adventure for Willard.	☐	☐	☐
	(B)	Willard intended to sail around the world by himself.	☐	☐	☐
	(C)	Willard was confident that he could achieve his goal.	☐	☐	☐
	(D)	Willard was raised far from the sea.	☐	☐	☐

			T	F	I
5.	(A)	The filament was mounted successfully on the first day.	☐	☐	☐
	(B)	The experimenters were patient and persistent workers.	☐	☐	☐
	(C)	When the current was turned on, the filament burned brightly.	☐	☐	☐
	(D)	Charles Bachelor was Thomas Edison's assistant.	☐	☐	☐

1.   Tom was still a bit nervous about his job. It was good, hard, outdoor work—the kind he liked. But he worried that he would do something wrong. Then he heard his boss's voice on the phone. "Tom, put the spruce saplings along the Clarks' property line in the back. Oh, and good job yesterday with reseeding at the Jasons." Tom smiled and relaxed.

---

2.   "The leaves are really colorful this year," Carmelita thought as she walked through the park. "Grandma so liked the fall season when she was here. The trees in her Puerto Rican homeland never turn brilliant colors like these." Carmelita continued her stroll. "I will write to Grandma soon, although not much has happened since my last letter." Then she paused, smiled to herself, and began collecting more leaves. These were the brightest colors, the most interesting shapes. "I remember Grandma helping me make a booklet of pressed leaves once," she reflected.

---

3.   This horse had never been ridden. The young newcomer, Lee, stood outside the corral, nervously watching the wild-eyed creature stomp along the inside perimeter. We're both afraid, Lee thought. I can see that. He inhaled the morning air deeply as he pulled on his new gloves. He heard the encouraging calls of the cowhands as he unlatched the gate. To gain their respect, Lee didn't have to stay on the horse long—but he had to show he could ride. "You can do it, Lee," called Sal. "You're smarter than that horse."

---

4.   Steve's parents were in the kitchen putting dishes, pots, and pans into the various cupboards and organizing them. Half-empty boxes were scattered about the room. "How was school, Steve?" his father asked as the young boy breezed into the room.

    "Not bad!" Steve answered enthusiastically. "I ate lunch with a couple of neat guys who live on the next street, and—guess what—there's a swimming pool in the school and they have a team, too! I'm trying out for it next week!"

---

5.   "Mom, won't you please buy some candles?" Terry begged. "I've spent two days making them, but no one will buy any. I've just *got* to make money so I can go to the World Series."

    Mrs. Norton looked at the misshapen candles. The wax was dirty and embedded with ants that had had the misfortune to fall into the melting pot. Smoky stripes completed the decorations. "Well," she said reluctantly, "I'll try one."

    The candle burned with a sputtering flame for about three seconds. Then the flame wilted, leaned sidewise, and went out.

UNIT 2

			T	F	I
1.	(A)	Tom enjoyed working outdoors.	□	□	□
	(B)	Tom is a gardener.	□	□	□
	(C)	Tom's boss gave him instructions over the phone.	□	□	□
	(D)	Tom's boss is not pleased with Tom's work.	□	□	□

			T	F	I
2.	(A)	Carmelita's grandmother's home is in Puerto Rico.	□	□	□
	(B)	Carmelita's grandmother had helped Carmelita become aware of the beauty of nature.	□	□	□
	(C)	Carmelita was planning to write to her grandmother soon.	□	□	□
	(D)	Carmelita would enclose some leaves in her next letter to Grandma.	□	□	□

			T	F	I
3.	(A)	Lee had never ridden a wild horse before this.	□	□	□
	(B)	Sal and the other cowhands offered encouragement to Lee.	□	□	□
	(C)	The other cowhands had already ridden this horse.	□	□	□
	(D)	Lee had to stay on the horse for hours to prove he could ride.	□	□	□

			T	F	I
4.	(A)	Steve had eaten lunch at home.	□	□	□
	(B)	Steve's family has just moved into a new home.	□	□	□
	(C)	There was a swimming pool in the school.	□	□	□
	(D)	Steve's parents were organizing things in the kitchen when Steve got home.	□	□	□

			T	F	I
5.	(A)	Terry did not have a good formula for making candles.	□	□	□
	(B)	Mrs. Norton bought ten candles.	□	□	□
	(C)	Terry wanted to go to the World Series.	□	□	□
	(D)	Terry had spent two weeks making the candles.	□	□	□

1.   "I just read about a Cherokee Indian who invented a system of 'talking leaves' in the late 1700s," said Lucia.

"Who was it, and what were 'talking leaves'?" asked Sean.

"It was Sequoya. He noticed that European settlers communicated with each other by way of written words, or 'talking leaves.' Sequoya then spent many years creating an alphabet of symbols. Although he faced difficulties, Sequoya was able to teach this system to the rest of the Cherokee nation," said Lucia.

---

2.   Grandmother Duzant took the sweet-potato pudding out of the oven and placed it next to the coconut drops cooling on the kitchen counter. Chicken and shrimp gumbo and beef dumplings had already been prepared. She hoped there would be enough food to satisfy the appetites of family and friends coming to keep her company at dinner late that afternoon. She glanced once again at the calendar; yes, she thought, she had much to be thankful for.

---

3.   Kari placed her artwork on the display board and stepped back, critically eyeing the painting she'd worked on for so long. "I've got to win the prize money for my painting," she said to her brother Bill. "It's the only way I'll ever have enough money to buy Mom the locket. I can't wait to see her face when she opens the locket and sees the picture," said Kari.

"She's sure to like it," said Bill, "but it'll probably bring a tear to her eye, as it would to mine, remembering Dad."

---

4.   Roger had purchased a new ten-speed bike, a sleek, silver model it had taken him six months to pay for. Now, every day after school, Roger could be found in the garage, avidly cleaning the wheels or shining the spokes.

"Don't you have anything better to do?" questioned Sally. "I never clean my bike, and it looks as good as new."

Roger couldn't help laughing as he glanced at Sally's bike. "If you say so," he said.

---

5.   Patrick was a very popular boy. He was friendly and fun-loving—qualities people liked. At school, students and teachers alike admired him. Usually these feelings were mutual. He was extremely kind to everyone he met. This was especially evident when new students came to school. Patrick would always go out of his way to make a newcomer feel welcome. No one was surprised when Patrick asked Laurene to have lunch with him and his friends.

UNIT 3

			T	F	I
1.	(A)	Sean was unfamiliar with "talking leaves."	☐	☐	☐
	(B)	The European settlers couldn't read or write.	☐	☐	☐
	(C)	Sequoya gave the Cherokees their first alphabet.	☐	☐	☐
	(D)	Sequoya used the same alphabet as the settlers.	☐	☐	☐

			T	F	I
2.	(A)	Coconut drops were cooling on the kitchen counter.	☐	☐	☐
	(B)	Relatives and friends were coming for lunch.	☐	☐	☐
	(C)	Grandmother Duzant lived alone.	☐	☐	☐
	(D)	It was Thanksgiving.	☐	☐	☐

			T	F	I
3.	(A)	Kari hopes to win a prize for her sculpture.	☐	☐	☐
	(B)	The children's father is no longer living.	☐	☐	☐
	(C)	Kari will probably put her Dad's picture in the locket for her mother.	☐	☐	☐
	(D)	Bill misses his dad.	☐	☐	☐

			T	F	I
4.	(A)	Roger kept his bike clean and shiny.	☐	☐	☐
	(B)	Sally cleaned her bike every day.	☐	☐	☐
	(C)	Roger knew his bike was much cleaner than Sally's.	☐	☐	☐
	(D)	Sally said her bike looked as good as new.	☐	☐	☐

			T	F	I
5.	(A)	Laurene is a new student at Patrick's school.	☐	☐	☐
	(B)	Patrick is not on good terms with the other students.	☐	☐	☐
	(C)	New students were always made to feel welcome by Patrick.	☐	☐	☐
	(D)	Everyone was surprised when Patrick asked Laurene to join him and his friends for lunch.	☐	☐	☐

1.   A "magalog" is a publication with characteristics of both a magazine and a catalog. Like a magazine, a magalog can have feature stories and outside advertising. Included in magalogs have been stories by W. Somerset Maugham and articles on car upkeep, gardening, and barbecuing. Like a catalog, a magalog spotlights the merchandise of the company that puts it out. One magalog had fifty-two pages of outside advertisements, feature stories, and showcasing of the company's products. Generally, however, magalogs are usually 16 to 19 pages long and sell for about $5.00. Many customers would rather buy a magalog than get a free catalog.

2.   African-American author Maya Angelou was born Marguerite Johnson in St. Louis, Missouri, in 1928 and was brought up by her grandmother in Stamps, Arkansas. Her famous book, *I Know Why the Caged Bird Sings*, is a reflection of her own childhood and growing-up experiences. A more recent book, *All God's Children Need Traveling Shoes*, is also autobiographical. It recounts Angelou's travels to Africa and her search for home. She wrote, "I knew my people had never completely left Africa. We had sung it in our blues, shouted it in our gospel, and danced the continent in our breakdowns."

3.   The blue willow pattern used on dishes tells the legend of a beautiful young Chinese woman, Koong-Shee, who fell in love with her father's male secretary, Chang. Koong-Shee's father asked his daughter to give up Chang for a rich man, but Koong-Shee refused. Her angry father put her into a small house at the end of the garden. Outside her window was a graceful willow tree. Finally Chang rescued Koong-Shee from the little house, taking her across a bridge to his house on the other side of the lake. Chang and Koong-Shee were married and lived happily until the rich man who had wanted to marry Koong-Shee killed the couple by burning their home.

4.   In Colonial Boston, young teenage boys often learned trades such as silversmithing and shipbuilding by becoming apprentices. An apprentice left his family's home and moved in with a master, someone who already practiced a trade. For several years, the apprentice worked for the master, learning about the trade through hands-on experience. The hours were long, and there was little time for entertainment, but the hardships were worthwhile. After apprenticeship, most tradesmen were able to practice on their own.

5.   Corinne looked pale as she left the telephone booth and hurried to the reservations desk with her luggage. "I must get a flight to New York as soon as possible," she said.
    "There's a flight leaving at midnight. There's one seat available," said the reservations clerk, "in the nonsmoking section."
    "Good. I'll take it. My name is Corinne Baron. I just came off your New York to London flight but must return to New York," said Corinne as she paid for her ticket. "When I get to Kennedy Airport, I'll take a taxi to the hospital," she thought.

UNIT 4

8 Sep

T F I

1. (A) Magalogs are never sold but are free to customers. ☐ ☐ ☐
   (B) A magalog is like a magazine because it has feature stories and outside advertising. ☐ ☐ ☐
   (C) A company can save money by publishing a magalog. ☐ ☐ ☐
   (D) A magalog is like a catalog because it spotlights the merchandise of the company that puts it out. ☐ ☐ ☐

T F I

2. (A) A restrictive childhood made Maya Angelou feel like a captive bird. ☐ ☐ ☐
   (B) Angelou was born in St. Louis, Missouri, in 1928. ☐ ☐ ☐
   (C) *All God's Children Need Traveling Shoes* is about Angelou and her travels in Africa. ☐ ☐ ☐
   (D) Angelou was reared in Arkansas by an aunt. ☐ ☐ ☐

T F I

3. (A) Chang was not a rich man. ☐ ☐ ☐
   (B) Koong-Shee fell in love with the rich man. ☐ ☐ ☐
   (C) A willow tree stood near the little house into which Koong-Shee's father put her. ☐ ☐ ☐
   (D) Koong-Shee and Chang were killed when their house was burned down. ☐ ☐ ☐

T F I

4. (A) Apprentices worked for their masters for a few years. ☐ ☐ ☐
   (B) Apprentices lived at home while they were learning their trade. ☐ ☐ ☐
   (C) It was important for apprentices to pay close attention to what their masters said and did. ☐ ☐ ☐
   (D) In Colonial Boston, many boys did not go to college. ☐ ☐ ☐

T F I

5. (A) It was unimportant to Corinne then whether the seat was in the nonsmoking or smoking section. ☐ ☐ ☐
   (B) Corinne got a seat on a plane leaving at midnight. ☐ ☐ ☐
   (C) Corinne had just flown from New York to Shannon. ☐ ☐ ☐
   (D) Someone dear to Corinne is in the hospital seriously ill or injured. ☐ ☐ ☐

UNIT 5

1.　"Why doesn't somebody do something about that lion in our yard?" Jan inquired of the family.

"Come on," said Mother and Father. "We're trying to watch television. You know very well there's no lion in the yard. Go back out and play."

No sooner had Jan's parents spoken these words when an announcer appeared on the television screen with a special message: "We interrupt this program to bring you word that a lion has escaped from the zoo. We repeat: A lion has escaped from the zoo!"

2.　Bobby reached upward, then fell back with a thud. He was sweating profusely; his body seemed to be on fire.

"I can't move my neck," he gasped. His shoulders were hunched on either side of his rigid neck. He moaned in pain and fear.

"He's very, very sick," said the doctor. "I've taken a spinal tap. It doesn't look good."

"Is it polio?" asked Bobby's mother, shrinking back as she mentioned the dreaded disease. She was quite sure she didn't want to hear the doctor's answer.

"Let's sit down and talk," said the doctor gravely. He needed time to think of how best to break the terrible news.

3.　Empress Josephine Bonaparte collected every known variety of rosebush from around the world to plant in her gardens at Malmaison near Paris, France. Even ships captured at sea by the French navy were searched for new species of roses. Then she commissioned the French artist Pierre Joseph Redouté to paint the 250 different kinds. After Josephine's death, the property containing the exquisite rose gardens changed hands several times and finally was largely destroyed in a battle. Yet the beauty of Malmaison lives on.

4.　Josephina promised her parents that she would improve her grades at school. "Don't worry," she said. "When the next report card comes, my grades will be higher."

For several weeks, Josephina spent many evening hours in her bedroom. One time, when the sounds of the music she played constantly were too loud, her mother asked her to lower the volume. Josephina did so. But next evening her music sounded even louder than before.

Days later, when the young student received her report card, she found that her grades had not improved at all.

5.　Huang and his sister were happy to have arrived safely in the United States. Now they would be able to attend school regularly, and their mother and father would be able to find good jobs. Maybe, they thought, they too would work, even if it meant that they would have to stay up late to do homework. Later, of course, they would attend college, earn good grades no matter what, and then go on to become doctors. Finally, they would return to their homeland to help others.

UNIT 5

8 Sep

			T	F	I
1.	(A)	A lion had escaped from the zoo.	☐	☐	☐
	(B)	At first, Mother and Father told Jan to go back out and play.	☐	☐	☐
	(C)	Jan only imagined that he had seen a lion in the yard.	☐	☐	☐
	(D)	Mother and Father believed Jan after they heard the television report.	☐	☐	☐

			T	F	I
2.	(A)	Bobby couldn't move his neck.	☐	☐	☐
	(B)	Bobby's mother asked the doctor if Bobby had polio.	☐	☐	☐
	(C)	Bobby was not in pain.	☐	☐	☐
	(D)	Bobby had a bad case of polio.	☐	☐	☐

			T	F	I
3.	(A)	The beauty of Josephine's rose gardens lives on in the paintings of Redouté.	☐	☐	☐
	(B)	Josephine collected 250 species of roses for her gardens.	☐	☐	☐
	(C)	Josephine's gardens are at Versailles, France.	☐	☐	☐
	(D)	The French navy searched ships captured at sea for new species of roses.	☐	☐	☐

			T	F	I
4.	(A)	The music had distracted Josephina as she studied.	☐	☐	☐
	(B)	Josephina told her parents not to worry about her school grades.	☐	☐	☐
	(C)	Josephina's mother asked Josephina to turn up the volume so the music could be heard.	☐	☐	☐
	(D)	The grades on Josephina's report card had not improved at all.	☐	☐	☐

			T	F	I
5.	(A)	The two youngsters' homeland offered few opportunities for success.	☐	☐	☐
	(B)	Huang and his sister were happy that they would be able to attend school regularly.	☐	☐	☐
	(C)	The youngsters' parents would be unable to work.	☐	☐	☐
	(D)	After they became doctors, Huang and his sister would return to their homeland.	☐	☐	☐

15

UNIT 6

1.   "We are out of food and ammunition," read the translated statement from the enemy. "We wish to surrender." The young lieutenant read the message again and rubbed his chin. He had seen trucks unloading behind the enemy lines yesterday. He also recalled an old war movie in which enemy soldiers had come forth with a white flag of surrender, all the while having machine guns strapped to their backs. With those guns they annihilated the Americans who stepped forward to receive them.

    "Tell them we accept their offer," ordered the lieutenant.

2.   With his fishing pole dangling from the rack behind him, fifteen-year-old Kenneth pedaled his bicycle at top speed. The sky was growing increasingly dark, and the air felt heavy. "It's going to start raining," he said aloud. "Tornado weather," he thought, pedaling faster. He had just left Murphy's Pond with his friend Manuel. Both boys were great fishers. They were always able to catch enough fish for dinner. Today they had not caught that many. Tonight's meal would be smaller than usual.

3.   "Step on the scale, Jimmy," said the white-coated doctor. The doctor adjusted the weights on the scale until they balanced.

    "How am I doing, Doc?" asked Jimmy.

    "Each week you do a little better," said the doctor, scribbling something on Jimmy's chart. "I'm going to change your medicine." The doctor wrote out a prescription and handed it to Jimmy. "This new protein drink should get you back up there more quickly."

4.   "I'm coming around the room to look at your homework, class," declared Mr. Appel.

    Roy's hand shot up. "May I leave the room?" he asked anxiously. "I just remembered that my mom asked me to make an important phone call."

    "I'm glad you remembered," said Mr. Appel. "It's easy to forget. And so that I won't forget to check your homework, let me see it before you go to make your call."

5.   Sam agreed to play after-school basketball with his friend Jeff at Jeff's junior high school. "I've never been to a junior high before," said Sam. "Will they let me in?"

    "No problem," said Jeff. "Try to look like a junior-high student. Just walk in as if you know your way around. The gym's right on the first floor."

    The next afternoon Sam entered the first-floor lobby of the junior high school. A teacher was standing there. "May I help you, sonny?" she asked.

UNIT 6

15 Sep 04

			T	F	I
1.	(A)	The enemy offered to give up the fight.	☐	☐	☐
	(B)	The lieutenant will order precautions against enemy trickery.	☐	☐	☐
	(C)	In an old war movie the enemy had come forth with a red flag.	☐	☐	☐
	(D)	The enemy message stated that they were out of food and ammunition.	☐	☐	☐

			T	F	I
2.	(A)	Kenneth was fifteen years old.	☐	☐	☐
	(B)	Kenneth's fishing pole was on his bicycle rack.	☐	☐	☐
	(C)	The boys had left the pond early because they saw signs of a storm approaching.	☐	☐	☐
	(D)	Manuel and Kenneth had caught no fish.	☐	☐	☐

			T	F	I
3.	(A)	Jimmy wants to gain weight.	☐	☐	☐
	(B)	Jimmy had never been to that doctor before.	☐	☐	☐
	(C)	The doctor was wearing a white coat.	☐	☐	☐
	(D)	Jimmy's new medicine is a protein drink.	☐	☐	☐

			T	F	I
4.	(A)	Mr. Appel asked for Roy's homework before letting him leave.	☐	☐	☐
	(B)	Roy outsmarted Mr. Appel.	☐	☐	☐
	(C)	Mr. Appel knew that Roy was trying to avoid having his homework checked.	☐	☐	☐
	(D)	Roy didn't really have to make a phone call.	☐	☐	☐

			T	F	I
5.	(A)	The gym was on the first floor.	☐	☐	☐
	(B)	The boys agreed to play basketball on Saturday morning.	☐	☐	☐
	(C)	Jeff attends the junior high.	☐	☐	☐
	(D)	Sam did not do a convincing job of looking like a junior-high-school student.	☐	☐	☐

In Unit 4, you read a passage about the legend behind the blue willow pattern used on dishes. Read the following passage about another legend—that of King Arthur and the Knights of the Round Table.

It is said that long ago there lived a great and noble king in the land of Britain. His name was Arthur. Arthur came to be king by drawing the magical sword Excalibur from a large rock—something that no one else had been able to do, though many had tried.

Once in power, Arthur gathered around him the bravest and strongest knights. They came together in Arthur's castle at Camelot. There they all sat at a round table, so that no one man would be at the head. Guided by the wise magician Merlin, Arthur planned how he and his knights would bring peace and prosperity to all the land.

A. Exercising Your Skill

What can you figure out about King Arthur's qualities, beliefs, and goals from what the passage tells you? Clues about characters are often revealed indirectly in stories. Often conversations, or dialogue, will help you figure out what the characters are like. Read the brief conversations below. On your paper, write one or two words or phrases to complete the statements that follow the dialogue. Your responses will be guesses based on information suggested in the passage.

"It won't be safe to enter that stronghold without help, Sire," said Gendyn. "We are clearly outnumbered."

"Thank you for your advice, Gendyn," replied Paxton. "We've come this far, though, and I don't think it's wise to leave the scroll in the hands of its captors very much longer. Our people's welfare depends on it."

One way to describe Gendyn is that he is _____ .

One way to describe Paxton is that he is _____ .

"This planet has not remained unexplored by mistake," grumbled Dr. Rovek. "Why don't we leave this desolate place and explore a planet that is worth our time?" he went on.

"Come, now, Rovek," responded Dr. Yov. "You know as well as I do that some of our greatest adventures have started out in situations just as unpromising as this. Now, shall we begin?"

One way to describe Dr. Rovek is that he is _____ .

One way to describe Dr. Yov is that she is _____ .

B. Expanding Your Skill

Rewrite one of the passages in Part A using information clues that would give readers a completely different idea about the personalities and values of the characters. Exchange rewritten passages with a classmate, and write new character statements like the ones in Part A— that is, "One way to describe _____ is that (s)he is _____ ."

C. Exploring Language

Look again at the passage about King Arthur and the Knights of the Round Table. Write these headings on your paper: <u>Directly Stated Information</u>, <u>Suggested Information</u>. Now write at least ten items of directly stated information under the first heading. Such information might be: *Arthur was king long ago.* Then write at least four ideas that are hinted at indirectly in the passage. Such suggested information might be: *Many people wanted to be king.* You can guess that because Arthur became king by drawing the sword from the stone, and many others had tried to do the same thing.

D. Expressing Yourself

Choose one of these activities.

1. Choose one of the following Aesop's fables, or choose one of your own favorites. Do library research if necessary to remind yourself of the details of the story. Then write a retelling of the fable. Include strong detail clues about characters' qualities, but do not name the qualities directly. Exchange fables with a classmate. Name the qualities of each character that can be inferred and identify the directly stated information that led to the inference.

   Some Aesop fables:

   "The Fox and the Grapes"
   "The Wolf in Sheep's Clothing"
   "The Goose That Laid the Golden Eggs"
   "The Shepherd Boy and the Wolf"
   "The Fox Without a Tail"
   "The Hare and the Tortoise"
   "The Town Mouse and the Country Mouse"
   "The Dog and the Wolf"

2. With three or four classmates make a skit out of one of Aesop's fables, or make up a fable of your own. Make sure the skit contains dialogue with both stated and suggested information. Perform the skit in front of a small group of classmates. After your performance, ask your audience to give a description of each character's personality and goals, based on what was stated or suggested in the skit.

1.   "It's time to choose parts for the class play," announced Mrs. Birns. "It helps if the character's personality matches the actor's," she continued. "Chris, I think you would be good as Romero. He's a heroic figure. And you, Nat, would probably understand the gentleness of the character Cassio. How do you two feel about taking those roles?" she asked.

"Sounds good," Chris and Nat responded in unison.

"Now, Sato," continued Mrs. Birns, "how about the role of the comical Tenisa?"

---

2.   "Why don't you join the three of us for lunch, Mary?" asked Katherine.

"I would, if I didn't have several important phone calls to make during the noon hour," replied Mary.

"Dick, John, and I are going to the new diner that has a telephone at each table. We won't mind your phoning. You can call anywhere you like, and the calls will be billed on your check."

"Then I'll come," agreed Mary. "I'll make the phone calls brief."

---

3.   Her name was Isabella, and she was born in Hurley, New York, about 1797. In her early adult years she was a slave. After she became free, she moved to New York City but couldn't earn a good living there. In 1843, Isabella changed her name to "Sojourner Truth."

"The spirit calls me," she said, "and I must go." Sojourner Truth began to travel and lecture. She became one of the greatest orators of her time. At her first few words her audiences became spellbound. In deep, though not loud tones, Sojourner Truth spoke for all human rights. Her remarks were often followed by cheering.

---

4.   The tick is an eight-legged relative of the spider. It will attach itself to you or to your pet and suck blood. Some species carry diseases. Colorado tick fever and relapsing fever are two such diseases common in the western half of the United States. Rocky Mountain spotted fever, which occurs throughout the United States, is more serious and sometimes fatal. All three kinds of tick fever have similar symptoms that appear about a week after a tick bite: high fever, headaches, nausea, vomiting, and sometimes muscle aches. With Rocky Mountain spotted fever, tiny pink dots appear around the wrists and ankles and eventually over the entire body.

---

5.   England's Warwick Castle has all that romantics associate with castles—including ghosts. The most conspicuous ghost is that of Sir Fulke Greville of the 1600s, who was bloodily murdered by his servant. Greville reportedly still walks the castle's Water Gate Tower. People have also glimpsed a Lady in Gray attempting to enter the castle's residential quarters. Who she may be is unknown. But a large black dog that roams the courtyard is said to be the transformed spirit of Nell Bloxham, who centuries ago leaped to death from one of the towers.

UNIT 7

			T	F	I
1.	(A)	Mrs. Birns thinks Sato has a comical personality.	☐	☐	☐
	(B)	Mrs. Birns thinks an actor can play any role equally well.	☐	☐	☐
	(C)	Mrs. Birns is assigning parts for the class play.	☐	☐	☐
	(D)	Chris and Nat agree with Mrs. Birns' choices for the characters of Romero and Cassio.	☐	☐	☐

			T	F	I
2.	(A)	Mary really wanted to visit and talk with her friends at the table.	☐	☐	☐
	(B)	Katherine planned to eat lunch at home.	☐	☐	☐
	(C)	Katherine asked Mary to join her and two others for lunch.	☐	☐	☐
	(D)	Dick and John did not plan to eat at the same diner.	☐	☐	☐

			T	F	I
3.	(A)	Sojourner Truth was born in New York City.	☐	☐	☐
	(B)	With only a few words, Sojourner Truth could make an audience spellbound.	☐	☐	☐
	(C)	Long-continued cheering frequently followed Sojourner Truth's statements.	☐	☐	☐
	(D)	Sojourner Truth gave hope to all discouraged people wherever she journeyed.	☐	☐	☐

			T	F	I
4.	(A)	A person with Rocky Mountain spotted fever gets pink dots around the wrists and ankles.	☐	☐	☐
	(B)	It is wise for a person who experiences nausea and vomiting following a tick bite to consult a doctor.	☐	☐	☐
	(C)	A tick is a six-legged insect that carries various diseases.	☐	☐	☐
	(D)	Colorado tick fever, relapsing fever, and Rocky Mountain spotted fever are three kinds of tick fever.	☐	☐	☐

			T	F	I
5.	(A)	Romantics enjoy the reports of existing ghosts at Warwick Castle.	☐	☐	☐
	(B)	No one is sure of the identity of the Lady in Gray.	☐	☐	☐
	(C)	Greville was murdered by his servant.	☐	☐	☐
	(D)	Nell Bloxham is the present owner of Warwick Castle.	☐	☐	☐

1.   "I'd like to improve your handwriting, Robin," said Mrs. Day.

"I have trouble keeping on the line," said Robin.

"Your letters could be formed more carefully too," replied Mrs. Day. "You're an 'open-house' writer. It's hard to tell what some of your letters are, since you don't always close them. When you write an *a*, it often looks like a *u* or *v*."

"Thanks, Mrs. Day," said Robin. "I'm going to try much harder to close all my letters. I really want to make my handwriting better."

2.   The people in the neighborhood leaned from their windows and cheered the youngsters playing ball in the street below. From time to time, the players stopped to let cars drive past. Some drivers were angry at the delay and honked their horns furiously. Nearby, two police officers in a patrol car sat and watched the game until one of the angry motorists approached them. "Why don't you do your job?" said the motorist. "You know it's illegal to play ball in the street."

3.   On May 5, 1930, Amy Johnson took off in a small, single-engine plane from England. She was on her way to Australia, trying to beat Bert Hinkler's record of just under sixteen days for the same flight. Her plans included stops each night for rest and refueling.

One problem after another spoiled her chance of beating Hinkler's record, but she did reach Australia on May 24. It had taken her nineteen days—three days longer than Hinkler. Even so, Johnson became known around the world as "Queen of the Skies."

4.   "Why do chickens contain light and dark meat, and ducks have only dark meat?" Mrs. Madison asked the butcher.

"Ducks fly; chickens really don't," replied the butcher. "Chickens only glide a few feet through the air."

"How does that affect the color of their meat?" asked Mrs. Madison.

"Birds that fly store a protein pigment in their muscles that gives them the energy to fly. This iron-containing pigment also gives the meat a darker color. Chickens have dark meat only in their thighs because they use their thigh muscles for walking," said the butcher.

5.   "I must get rid of the dandelions on our lawn," said Mr. Didato.

"I just read how nutritious they are," declared his wife. "Before you poison them, let me gather some young shoots. They contain more vitamin A than any cultivated vegetable, including carrots."

"Very interesting," said Mr. Didato. "Please help yourself!"

"Thanks," said Mrs. Didato. "Dandelions have as much iron as spinach and are also rich in thiamin, riboflavin, and calcium."

"In that case," replied her husband, "maybe I'll buy some dandelion seed to plant in rows near our corn, potatoes, and beans."

ZZ Sep. 04

		T	F	I

1.   (A)   Mrs. Day is Robin's teacher.   ☐ ☐ ☐
     (B)   Robin has a good attitude at school.   ☐ ☐ ☐
     (C)   Mrs. Day criticized Robin for not crossing her *t*'s.   ☐ ☐ ☐
     (D)   Mrs. Day called Robin an "open-house" writer.   ☐ ☐ ☐

                     T   F   I

2.   (A)   The police officers were sympathetic toward the ballplayers.   ☐ ☐ ☐
     (B)   Two motorists approached the police officers.   ☐ ☐ ☐
     (C)   The spectators encouraged the ballplayers.   ☐ ☐ ☐
     (D)   The drivers of the cars were anxious to reach their destinations.   ☐ ☐ ☐

                     T   F   I

3.   (A)   Bert Hinkler was a well-known early aviator.   ☐ ☐ ☐
     (B)   Johnson had planned a nonstop flight from England to Australia.   ☐ ☐ ☐
     (C)   It took Johnson nineteen days to fly from England to Australia.   ☐ ☐ ☐
     (D)   A single-engine plane carried Johnson from England to Australia.   ☐ ☐ ☐

                     T   F   I

4.   (A)   Mrs. Madison buys both chickens and ducks from the butcher.   ☐ ☐ ☐
     (B)   A pigment containing iron gives meat a darker color.   ☐ ☐ ☐
     (C)   Ducks contain only light meat.   ☐ ☐ ☐
     (D)   Chickens have dark meat only in their thighs.   ☐ ☐ ☐

                     T   F   I

5.   (A)   Carrots contain more vitamin A than dandelions.   ☐ ☐ ☐
     (B)   Mrs. Didato had read about the nutritional value of dandelions.   ☐ ☐ ☐
     (C)   The Didatos have a vegetable garden.   ☐ ☐ ☐
     (D)   Spinach and dandelions contain the same amount of iron.   ☐ ☐ ☐

UNIT 9

1.   When thinking of early electronics, not many people think of Nikola Tesla. Yet, it was this Yugoslavian-born engineer who first designed a practical system for generating and transmitting alternating current for electric power. Tesla sold the rights to this invention to George Westinghouse, and then he continued his own research. Tesla contributed much to the field of wireless communication. Ahead of his time, he even attempted wireless communication with planets other than Earth.

2.   "I can't do it," exclaimed Harold. "No matter how much I want to, I just can't jump from the high diving board."

Maryanne smiled at her friend. "Of course you can," she responded. "All you have to do is make up your mind that it's possible. The rest is easy."

Now feeling confident, Harold turned, climbed up the ladder, and stepped to the edge of the diving board. Then, however, in the back of his mind, he remembered what his friend Ian had said earlier.

3.   Mercedes danced rhythmically to the music as her partner, Paul, led her in the intricate steps. They both knew that they had never really expected to attend the dance together. And they realized, also, that they would probably never again go out on a date. After all, they were nothing more than acquaintances. Nevertheless, they were enjoying themselves. But when Paul looked intently across the dance floor and smiled eagerly, Mercedes followed her partner's gaze over to her friend Carol. Carol was dancing with Paul's brother.

4.   No matter how hard she looked, Marcella couldn't find the box of pins she needed to complete her project for school. "What will I do if I can't find them?" she thought. "I won't be able to finish on time."

Now almost desperate, Marcella rushed from aisle to aisle in the small store. Sometimes she even visited the same aisle twice. She knew that if she handed her project in late, Mrs. Callacio would give a low grade.

Then, when Marcella was almost ready to give up, she saw a little blue and red box labeled *Pins* sitting on the shelf right in front of her.

5.   Kirstin was excited at the thought of her cousin's upcoming visit to Pennsylvania. Of course, she and Ilse had known about each other for many years. But this would be the first time they would meet. "Do you think Ilse will enjoy her stay with us?" she asked her mother.

Her mother smiled. "Of course she will. But she might have quite a few problems getting around. We'll help her as much as we can. After all, this will be the first time she'll be so far away from home."

UNIT 9

22 Sep 04

		T	F	I
1.	(A) Tesla believed that other planets were inhabited.	☐	☐	☐
	(B) Tesla did not work on wireless communication.	☐	☐	☐
	(C) Nikola Tesla invented a system for generating alternating electrical current.	☐	☐	☐
	(D) Tesla continued his own research after he invented his alternating current system.	☐	☐	☐

		T	F	I
2.	(A) Ian had discouraged Harold from jumping.	☐	☐	☐
	(B) Harold felt confident after he spoke to Maryanne.	☐	☐	☐
	(C) Maryanne encouraged Harold.	☐	☐	☐
	(D) At the end of the story, Harold did not want to jump from the diving board.	☐	☐	☐

		T	F	I
3.	(A) Paul was interested in dancing with Carol.	☐	☐	☐
	(B) Mercedes and Paul planned to go out on more dates.	☐	☐	☐
	(C) Mercedes followed Paul's gaze over to Carol.	☐	☐	☐
	(D) Mercedes perceived Paul's brother as her next dancing partner.	☐	☐	☐

		T	F	I
4.	(A) Mrs. Callacio is a strict teacher.	☐	☐	☐
	(B) Marcella felt that Mrs. Callacio wouldn't mind if her project were handed in late.	☐	☐	☐
	(C) The pins were in a blue and red box.	☐	☐	☐
	(D) Marcella was not as observant as she might have been.	☐	☐	☐

		T	F	I
5.	(A) Ilse is disabled in some way.	☐	☐	☐
	(B) The two girls found out about each other recently.	☐	☐	☐
	(C) Kirstin's mother said they would help Ilse get around.	☐	☐	☐
	(D) Ilse had been far away from home on several occasions.	☐	☐	☐

1.   Have you ever wondered if there is life in other solar systems? According to scientists, there could be life elsewhere in the universe, but no one is certain. So far, Earth's scientists have discovered no signals from space that might come from extraterrestrial civilizations. Because the path of development of life is so long and complex, there is little chance of its having progressed identically on two worlds.

2.   Cannon smoke obscured the sunless battlefield on which two opposing armies faced each other. Well-trained and lined up in straight ranks, the soldiers of one army waited confidently for the attack. Less disciplined but determined to win, the soldiers of the second army advanced up a steep hill. The odds, they knew, were not in their favor.

After the battle ended, officers from the second army visited the site. Smiling broadly, one of the officers said, "As you can see, courageous volunteers can often win battles even if the odds are against them."

3.   "I'm very concerned about Bridget, dear," Mr. Josephson said to his wife. "As you know, her teacher says that she's much too quiet. She never participates in class discussions, and she prefers to work alone rather than in groups."

Mrs. Josephson looked up from the book she was reading and smiled wryly. "Well," she responded, "that's true enough, Dave. But I think I know why. I can remember when my grandmother used to say that the apple never falls far from the tree."

4.   Harold sat hunched in his seat on the bus shortly after it pulled out of his hometown. Peering out the window to his right, he gazed at the great, flat fields of corn in Iowa. Everywhere he looked, green stalks pushed upward from the ground. Then, in the distance, Harold saw the tiny figure of a man riding on what seemed a miniature tractor. For a moment, the seventeen-year-old boy felt lonely and sad. Perhaps, he thought, he should have waited just a little longer.

5.   Mr. Spiva gripped the car's wheel tightly. For many weeks, he had been taking driving lessons. Now, as he prepared to take his final driving test, he wondered if he would pass. Turning the wheel sharply, he pressed the accelerator pedal and lurched into the traffic.

Twenty minutes later, Mr. Spiva managed to work his way into a parking space. He smiled at the examiner sitting next to him. "How did I do?" he asked the perspiring woman, who smiled back at him weakly.

UNIT 10

22 Sep 04

			T	F	I
1.	(A)	Scientists say that there could be life elsewhere in the universe.	□	□	□
	(B)	Any beings elsewhere in the universe are not going to look like humans.	□	□	□
	(C)	There have been no signals from space that might have come from extraterrestrial civilizations.	□	□	□
	(D)	Life's path of development is long and complex.	□	□	□

29 Sep 04

			T	F	I
2.	(A)	The soldiers of the well-trained army did not perform as well as was expected.	□	□	□
	(B)	The battle was fought on a bright, sunny day.	□	□	□
	(C)	The soldiers of the second army advanced along a level field.	□	□	□
	(D)	The men of the well-trained army waited confidently.	□	□	□

			T	F	I
3.	(A)	Mrs. Josephson feels that Mr. Josephson once had the same problem Bridget has.	□	□	□
	(B)	Mr. Josephson is not concerned about how Bridget performs in school.	□	□	□
	(C)	Mrs. Josephson was reading a book.	□	□	□
	(D)	Bridget prefers to work in groups with other children.	□	□	□

			T	F	I
4.	(A)	Harold knew the man on the tractor.	□	□	□
	(B)	The bus was hundreds of miles from Harold's hometown.	□	□	□
	(C)	The story took place in Idaho.	□	□	□
	(D)	Harold was seventeen years old.	□	□	□

			T	F	I
5.	(A)	Mr. Spiva did not pass the driving exam.	□	□	□
	(B)	The examiner was perspiring.	□	□	□
	(C)	Mr. Spiva drove smoothly throughout the exam.	□	□	□
	(D)	The examiner had been concerned about getting into an accident.	□	□	□

1.   I met Jane because of our mutual interest in dirt bikes. Not many women are involved in this sport. Anyway, Jane has two bikes—a Japanese bike like mine and an expensive French bike. She likes the French bike best, but it's very temperamental. It's always breaking down, is hard to find parts for, and is expensive to repair. Still, she prefers it over the Japanese bike, especially for racing. Yet, today is the big race of the season, and I just saw Jane drive by in her pick-up truck. The Japanese bike was strapped in the truck.

2.   Mary Lou and her father had taken the things they needed: camera, extra film, and sandwiches. They both knew a lot about the animals that lived in the forest, and both were especially good at recognizing animal tracks. "Look over here, Mary Lou," whispered her father when they entered the forest. "I think these tracks belong to a fox."

Mary Lou looked down to see the prints in the soft, wet earth. "Yes," she said, "let's follow them."

3.   Hyoun Lee had lived in the city for five years. Colin, the first neighbor he had met when he arrived, was still his best friend. The boys had many things in common, including a love of skateboarding.

"Hey, Colin, I'll beat you to the fountain in the middle of the park," challenged Hyoun.

"Finally, my big chance," said Colin with an impish grin. "I'm bound to win with my new skateboard."

"Don't bet on it," shouted Hyoun as he pushed off.

4.   For the first time in months at sea, Stacy gave in to a feeling of homesickness. The ship was standing well offshore of a sailing village that reminded her of the coastline near her home. Because she had practically grown up on a boat, it had seemed natural for her to choose a nautical career. Just now, though, her view of wharves and yachts was limited to what she could see through a periscope. But, she reminded herself, it had been her choice. Straightening, she gave the order to lower the periscope.

5.   Dawn was the signal for the two great fleets to begin the battle. When, hours later, the young man saw the flames engulf the mainsail of his ship, he realized that the whole vessel would soon be ablaze. Diving over the starboard side, he floundered in the water until he felt powerful arms pulling him aboard a lifeboat. Raising his head to thank his rescuers, he was startled to realize that the officers' uniforms were not those of the English navy. These stronghearted sailors were Spanish!

UNIT 11

			T	F	I
1.	(A)	The Japanese bike is Jane's favorite.	☐	☐	☐
	(B)	Jane's French bike has broken down again.	☐	☐	☐
	(C)	Today is the big race of the season.	☐	☐	☐
	(D)	According to the author, few women are involved in dirt-bike racing.	☐	☐	☐

			T	F	I
2.	(A)	Mary Lou and her father had taken sandwiches with them.	☐	☐	☐
	(B)	Mary Lou suggested they follow the footprints her father had spotted.	☐	☐	☐
	(C)	Mary Lou thought the tracks belonged to a fox.	☐	☐	☐
	(D)	It had rained recently.	☐	☐	☐

			T	F	I
3.	(A)	Colin had a new skateboard.	☐	☐	☐
	(B)	Colin had moved to the city a year ago.	☐	☐	☐
	(C)	Hyoun usually wins the skateboard races.	☐	☐	☐
	(D)	Colin and Hyoun are friends.	☐	☐	☐

			T	F	I
4.	(A)	Stacy saw her own hometown through the periscope.	☐	☐	☐
	(B)	Stacy had often been on a boat prior to choosing a nautical career.	☐	☐	☐
	(C)	Stacy is a naval officer on a submarine.	☐	☐	☐
	(D)	Stacy was feeling homesick.	☐	☐	☐

			T	F	I
5.	(A)	The young man was in the English navy.	☐	☐	☐
	(B)	English sailors rescued the young man from the water.	☐	☐	☐
	(C)	The young man became a prisoner.	☐	☐	☐
	(D)	The young man saw the mainsail of his ship go up in flames.	☐	☐	☐

1.   "Come on! Will you move it?" Mr. Williams shouted out his car window. Then he honked his horn at the car ahead. Again he yelled out his window. "Can't you see you're holding up traffic?"

Then Mr. Williams saw what the problem was. A big blue car was broken down in front of the car ahead of him. Mr. Williams was ashamed that he had honked and yelled. He got out and helped push the stalled car off to the side of the road.

---

2.   Mrs. Bond slapped vehemently at another mosquito. "Darn it!" she said. "Why aren't these annoying little insects bothering you at all?" As Mrs. Bond scratched an itchy bump on the back of her neck, she looked at Mrs. Stephens.

"I thought you had already put some of this on at home," said Mrs. Stephens. "I'm sorry I didn't give this to you earlier." She handed Mrs. Bond a plastic bottle.

"Well, I guess that's my answer," said Mrs. Bond. "Insect repellent."

---

3.   "I just saw a star fall right out of the sky," said Cliff.

"That's impossible," said Thelma. "Stars are millions of miles away. You couldn't have seen anything of the sort."

"Wait a second. I don't want you two to start arguing again. Let me explain," said Mr. McCoy. "What Cliff saw is sometimes called a shooting star because that's what it looks like. It's also called a meteor. Meteors are just chunks of rock from space. They heat up and glow when they come into the air above the earth."

---

4.   "I heard that Stan is hiding something important in his desk," whispered Fran.

"I'd like to find out what he really does have in that desk of his," said Dan.

After class, when everyone had left, Fran and Dan crept quietly to Stan's desk. Dan held open the top while Fran peeked inside. "All that's in there is a pile of books," said Fran.

Just then, the teacher walked in. "What do you children think you're doing looking in someone else's desk?" she asked angrily.

---

5.   "I don't care at all for Philip Davis," said Art. "He's a bigmouth, and all he talks about is himself."

"That's been my opinion of him, too," said Yvonne. "He's very arrogant."

Just then Philip Davis came along. "That really is a good-looking shirt you're wearing," Philip told Art. "Where do you get your clothes?"

As Art answered the question, he was not certain that he disliked Philip Davis anymore.

Yvonne stood there with her mouth open in amazement. Was this the same Philip Davis they had just talked about, she wondered.

UNIT 12

		T	F	I

1. (A) The driver in front of Mr. Williams was not reacting to the honking and yelling. ☐ ☐ ☐
    (B) The driver of the stalled car did not allow Mr. Williams to help. ☐ ☐ ☐
    (C) The car that had stalled was blue. ☐ ☐ ☐
    (D) Mr. Williams would apologize to the driver of the car directly ahead of him for honking and yelling. ☐ ☐ ☐

		T	F	I

2. (A) Mrs. Stephens refused to give Mrs. Bond the bottle of repellent. ☐ ☐ ☐
    (B) Mrs. Bond scratched an itchy bump on the back of her neck. ☐ ☐ ☐
    (C) Mrs. Bond couldn't understand why the mosquitoes were bothering only her. ☐ ☐ ☐
    (D) Mrs. Bond was glad that Mrs. Stephens had brought insect repellent along. ☐ ☐ ☐

		T	F	I

3. (A) Mr. McCoy didn't want Cliff and Thelma to argue. ☐ ☐ ☐
    (B) Neither Thelma nor Cliff knew what meteors are. ☐ ☐ ☐
    (C) Cliff didn't actually see a star fall from the sky. ☐ ☐ ☐
    (D) Thelma and Cliff often argue about different things. ☐ ☐ ☐

		T	F	I

4. (A) For Fran and Dan, looking inside the desk was not worth the trouble they got into. ☐ ☐ ☐
    (B) Fran and Dan found only books in Stan's desk. ☐ ☐ ☐
    (C) Fran and Dan didn't want anyone to see them peek into Stan's desk. ☐ ☐ ☐
    (D) The teacher didn't notice that Fran and Dan were looking into Stan's desk. ☐ ☐ ☐

		T	F	I

5. (A) Initially, Art and Yvonne agreed that Philip Davis was soft-spoken and considerate of others. ☐ ☐ ☐
    (B) Philip complimented Art on his shirt. ☐ ☐ ☐
    (C) Philip Davis was trying to change his image. ☐ ☐ ☐
    (D) Yvonne's mouth was open in amazement. ☐ ☐ ☐

"I'm very concerned about Bridget, dear," Mr. Josephson said to his wife. "As you know, her teacher says that she's much too quiet. She never participates in class discussions, and she prefers to work alone rather than in groups."

Mrs. Josephson looked up from the book she was reading and smiled wryly. "Well," she responded, "that's true enough, Dave. But I think I know why. I can remember when my grandmother used to say that the apple never falls far from the tree."

A. Exercising Your Skill

The passage above lets you know that Bridget is a shy person. The word *shy* isn't used, but phrases like "much too quiet," "never participates in class discussions," and "prefers to work alone rather than in groups" give you plenty of clues as to her personality. Stories often tell about a character's personality through descriptive words and by letting you know how the character responds in different situations. Practice identifying these types of clues. For each situation below, think of how a shy person would probably act and how an outgoing person would probably act. In your answers, you can include what they say as well as what they do.

- walking into a new classroom on the first day in a new school—
  A shy person would probably . . .   An outgoing person would probably . . .
- meeting someone that he or she has admired for a long time—
  A shy person would probably . . .   An outgoing person would probably . . .
- accepting an award in front of a large audience—
  A shy person would probably . . .   An outgoing person would probably . . .
- responding to a teacher's request for volunteers to work on the class play—
  A shy person would probably . . .   An outgoing person would probably . . .

B. Expanding Your Skill

On your paper, create a word web for *shy* and for *outgoing*. Choose words from the box that relate to *shy* or to *outgoing*, and write them on the webs on your paper. You may want to start your webs like the ones below. After you have used the words in the box, add other words that you know.

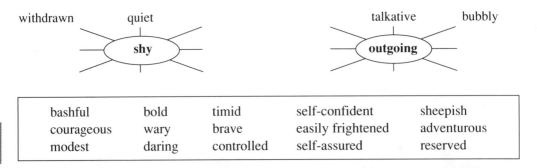

withdrawn	quiet		talkative	bubbly
	shy		**outgoing**	

bashful	bold	timid	self-confident	sheepish
courageous	wary	brave	easily frightened	adventurous
modest	daring	controlled	self-assured	reserved

C. Exploring Language

Read the following situations. Choose one of them and continue it. Or, if you prefer, develop a situation on your own. Include indirect suggestions in your story as well as directly stated information about the main character's personality. Write the story on your paper.

Before you begin to write, you may want to list your ideas for the story as follows:

Main idea: _____
Stated character details: _____ _____ _____
Suggested character details: _____ _____ _____
Action details: _____ _____ _____
Conclusion: _____

Situations

•   "We are now going to form groups to do research for our 'Foods of Different Cultures' project," announced Miss Gaines.
      "Oh, no," moaned Adam to himself. "It's so awful not knowing anyone yet. I hate being a new student." Adam lowered his eyes and prepared for the worst.

•   "Now," said the master of ceremonies at Junior Magicians' Night, "do we have any junior magicians in the audience who want to show us their stuff?"
      "Boy! Am I glad I brought my wand!" thought Wendy as she jumped out of her seat.

D. Expressing Yourself

Choose one of these activities.

1. With a group of classmates think of a story you have all read. Then think of another story in which the main character was a very different kind of person from the main character in the first story. Orally compare and contrast the two characters. Give examples of dialogue and actions that tell about their personalities. Then retell each story with the main characters switched. Show how each story and its conclusion would change.

2. With a partner, pantomime different personality traits, qualities, or moods: *shy*, *outgoing*, *angry*, *friendly*, *grumpy*, *snooty*, and so forth. Have your classmates guess each trait after you have mimed it.

1.　"Well, there go the lights," said Father. "It was bound to happen sooner or later in a windstorm like this."

"I'm hungry. Let's cook something on the stove while we're waiting for the lights to come back on," suggested Cathy.

"The stove is electric," said Father. "All the electricity is out."

"We can get food from the refrigerator," said Cathy.

"The refrigerator runs on electricity, too," said Father. "We'd better not open the door, or all the cold air will escape."

"I hate not having electricity," moaned Cathy.

Just then the lights came back on.

2.　"Why do you think people started making buildings taller in northeastern cities in the early 1900s?" asked Mr. Jacobsen.

"Didn't a lot of people move to the cities to find jobs around that time?" ventured Pete.

"Yes," responded Mr. Jacobsen, "and as the cities got more crowded, more room was needed. Expansion then took place in the only direction that was left—up." The teacher continued, "Can you think of how the mass production of steel around that time added to the growth of tall buildings?"

3.　"I don't believe in things that haven't been proved to exist," said Linda. "You can believe in flying saucers, but I think it's silly."

"Wait!" advised Phyllis. "The fact that a thing hasn't been proved doesn't mean that it can't exist. Before there were microscopes, nobody thought thousands of tiny animals were in a drop of pond water."

"That may be true," agreed Linda, "but many people have believed in things that never have existed and never will. Look at the hoaxes that have fooled millions of people. I can't be taken in."

4.　"Minh didn't exaggerate when he said that the hurricane did enormous damage," said Karen. "Look at those cars that were destroyed by falling trees. Dozens of homes were damaged, too."

"Yes," said Julia, "the hurricane was destructive, but when I think of how that radio announcer scared us just before the storm hit, I shudder. At least there were no serious injuries or deaths."

5.　"They don't make them like this anymore," said Stan as he ran his hand along the side of his car. "Everything on it is original, from the fenders down to the paint job."

"Yes, it's a beauty indeed," agreed Norma.

"Would you like a ride?" asked Stan.

"Well," said Norma, "are you sure it's safe?"

"Safe?" Stan looked puzzled. "Of course it's safe. Just look ɑ　"

Norma glanced nervously at the car. "I'd love a ride, Stan," ɹe said, "but I'm afraid I'll be late for dinner if I take one now."

2 0 Oct. 09

			T	F	I
1.	(A)	Cathy didn't know the stove was run by electricity.	☐	☐	☐
	(B)	The electricity was off for many hours.	☐	☐	☐
	(C)	Father didn't want cold air to escape from the refrigerator.	☐	☐	☐
	(D)	The lights went out during a snowstorm.	☐	☐	☐

			T	F	I
2.	(A)	There were already a lot of buildings in cities by the early 1900s.	☐	☐	☐
	(B)	In the 1900s, many people moved to northeastern cities to find jobs.	☐	☐	☐
	(C)	Cities were not very crowded in the 1900s.	☐	☐	☐
	(D)	Steel was mass-produced in the early 1900s.	☐	☐	☐

			T	F	I
3.	(A)	Phyllis believes that someday scientists will prove that flying saucers do exist.	☐	☐	☐
	(B)	Linda pointed out that hoaxes have fooled millions of people.	☐	☐	☐
	(C)	Linda does not believe in ghosts.	☐	☐	☐
	(D)	Linda thinks it's silly to believe in flying saucers.	☐	☐	☐

			T	F	I
4.	(A)	Minh didn't exaggerate about the hurricane damage.	☐	☐	☐
	(B)	Karen said that dozens of homes had been damaged.	☐	☐	☐
	(C)	Trees had not fallen on any cars.	☐	☐	☐
	(D)	The radio announcer had predicted that many people would die in a "killer" storm.	☐	☐	☐

			T	F	I
5.	(A)	Stan's car was probably an antique.	☐	☐	☐
	(B)	Norma made an excuse because she had doubts about the car's safety.	☐	☐	☐
	(C)	Stan invited Norma to go for a ride in his car.	☐	☐	☐
	(D)	Norma said she was afraid of being late for her doctor's appointment.	☐	☐	☐

1. Jimmy looked at his new watch as it beeped a warning. Suzie would be late again. He studied the silver watch and reset the alarm. He checked its calendar again. Jimmy was proud of that watch. It would have gotten him to the movie on time if he hadn't arranged to meet Suzie. He loved murder mysteries. Jimmy stared at the watch, counting the seconds. When Suzie arrived, he'd be able to tell her exactly how late she was.

And then, there she was. "Right on time," she said as the very accurate clock in the church tower began to chime.

---

2. Betsy was almost two years old, and her brother Bobby was five. Their playroom was closed off with a latched, folding gate that the manufacturer had labeled "childproof." This let their mother work in the kitchen and still see what was going on in the playroom. One day she went to the cellar to transfer the wash into the dryer. When she returned to the kitchen, she found Betsy sitting on the kitchen floor playing with the cat. Bobby was sitting at the table, eating a banana.

---

3. Mrs. Glenn, the school superintendent, sat in her office and watched the snowflakes swirling around in the blustery wind. In the past hour the snowfall had become heavier, and the school playground was now buried under four inches. She now had to decide whether or not to close the schools early. Were the roads going to be safe for the buses to travel on, or were they becoming impassable? "There's only one way to find out," she thought as she reached for the telephone.

---

4. Dear Alfie,

I am thirteen years old. Susan has been my best friend for five years. This year, however, we seem to have developed a lot of differences. For instance, I want to have other friends in addition to Susan. She wants to stay "just the two of us." I feel guilty. What do you suggest?

(signed) Confused

---

5. For the past hour the earth beneath Aaron's feet had been muddy, making the trek through the jungle frustrating and slow. But now the situation underfoot had changed. Somehow, this mud was not the same. A look of panic crossed Aaron's face. Cautiously, he moved forward. A curious, sucking noise accompanied each sticky footstep. Suddenly, Aaron's boots began to sink, despite his efforts to lift them. The relentless sucking noises continued.

10 Nov. 04

		T	F	I
1.	(A) Jimmy's watch was silver.	☐	☐	☐
	(B) Jimmy was proud of his watch.	☐	☐	☐
	(C) Suzie was early.	☐	☐	☐
	(D) Jimmy and Suzie often went places together.	☐	☐	☐

		T	F	I
2.	(A) The children's mother went to the cellar.	☐	☐	☐
	(B) The gate was not really "childproof."	☐	☐	☐
	(C) Bobby is younger than Betsy.	☐	☐	☐
	(D) The children had managed to unlock the gate.	☐	☐	☐

		T	F	I
3.	(A) The snowfall had decreased in the past hour.	☐	☐	☐
	(B) Mrs. Glenn watched the snow falling from her office.	☐	☐	☐
	(C) There were four inches of snow on the playground.	☐	☐	☐
	(D) Mrs. Glenn would call the bus company.	☐	☐	☐

		T	F	I
4.	(A) The writer feels both guilty and confused.	☐	☐	☐
	(B) The writer wants to have other friends.	☐	☐	☐
	(C) Susan and the writer just met this year.	☐	☐	☐
	(D) Susan is jealous of the writer's other friends.	☐	☐	☐

		T	F	I
5.	(A) Aaron was stepping into quicksand.	☐	☐	☐
	(B) All the mud seemed the same to Aaron.	☐	☐	☐
	(C) Aaron managed to avoid the mud.	☐	☐	☐
	(D) Aaron traveled slowly and with difficulty through the jungle.	☐	☐	☐

1.   Hundreds of fans had turned out for what was to be John Peters' last performance. Singing the role that he had made famous nearly fifty years ago, Peters faltered only slightly on the extended notes. At the end of the performance, Peters received a standing ovation from his loyal fans, a tribute to a career that had spanned several generations. Later, one critic would sum up the feeling of most who had attended: "At least he sang with gusto."

---

2.   Frank gnashed his teeth as he sat behind the wheel of his bright red sports car. His fingers played a drum beat on the leather-covered steering wheel, and his feet tapped a nervous rhythm on the plush, custom-made carpeting. He thought about honking his horn but realized how useless that would be; cars were lined up on the highway as far as the eye could see. He pushed the radio buttons one after another, unable to find a song to his liking. "It will be hours before I get home," he thought disgustedly.

---

3.   Can you imagine gardens that never need watering? The early Aztec people built just such gardens. Guided by a religious sign, the Aztecs settled on a small island in the middle of a lake. To survive, they wove reed mats, covered them with soil, and planted seeds in the soil. They placed these sprouting mats on the lake to create floating gardens—with a continuous supply of water!

---

4.   Despairingly, Carole eyed the stack of dirty dishes piled on the kitchen counter. It was her turn to clean up, but she couldn't seem to motivate herself. Sighing, Carole looked out the window at the falling leaves. Although her mother had asked her to rake the lawn, Carole had decided that it made no sense to rake leaves until all the trees were bare. After all, she said, why do the same job twice? Carole sighed again as she remembered her mother's disapproving look. "You think of an excuse for everything," her mother had scolded.

---

5.   It was 8:30 A.M., much later than the governor usually slept. She and two advisors had been up late, mulling over possible reactions to the speech she had delivered and possible steps to take if the reactions were bad. She dressed quickly and went to her office, where copies of the morning newspapers would be on her desk along with a light breakfast. Even before she got to her desk, she noticed her secretary with the newspapers spread open in front of him and a distressed look on his face.

UNIT 15

5 Jan. 09

			T	F	I
1.	(A)	John Peters' voice was not what it used to be.	☐	☐	☐
	(B)	As his farewell concert ended, Peters was honored by the audience.	☐	☐	☐
	(C)	Only a few fans attended the last performance of John Peters.	☐	☐	☐
	(D)	John Peters sang the role that he had made famous.	☐	☐	☐

			T	F	I
2.	(A)	Frank's sports car was red.	☐	☐	☐
	(B)	Frank began to honk his horn.	☐	☐	☐
	(C)	Frank was an impatient person.	☐	☐	☐
	(D)	Many cars were lined up on the highway in front of Frank.	☐	☐	☐

			T	F	I
3.	(A)	Seeds were planted on reed mats that were then floated on the lake.	☐	☐	☐
	(B)	The early Aztecs were determined to stay on their new island home.	☐	☐	☐
	(C)	The early Aztecs knew nothing about gardening.	☐	☐	☐
	(D)	Aztec people had faith in religious signs.	☐	☐	☐

			T	F	I
4.	(A)	It was springtime.	☐	☐	☐
	(B)	Carole had decided to wait until all the leaves were off the trees.	☐	☐	☐
	(C)	There were dirty dishes on the kitchen counter.	☐	☐	☐
	(D)	Carole doesn't enjoy doing chores around the house.	☐	☐	☐

			T	F	I
5.	(A)	The governor went to sleep right after speaking.	☐	☐	☐
	(B)	The governor dressed quickly.	☐	☐	☐
	(C)	Reactions to the governor's speech were bad.	☐	☐	☐
	(D)	The governor usually slept until 8:30.	☐	☐	☐

1.   "Do you know where my coat is?" Jennifer asked her mother. "I need to find it—and fast."

"What's the big rush?" asked Mrs. Cramer. "Do you have plans?"

"No, but I've got to be out of the house by three," answered Jennifer, "when Matt starts practicing on his trumpet."

"Well, you could come out and sit on the porch, as I do. The sound is not that blaring out there," suggested Mrs. Cramer.

"No, I just would rather stay away altogether," said Jennifer.

---

2.   All night Nicole couldn't sleep. By morning, she felt twice as tired as before she had gone to bed. "This is ridiculous," Nicole mumbled half out loud. "I'll just get it over with."

When Nicole got to school, she went straight to her friend Lorraine. "I want to apologize for losing my temper yesterday," said Nicole. "I was having a bad day. I didn't mean to take it out on you."

"Oh, don't give it another thought," said Lorraine. "I had already forgotten the whole incident."

---

3.   "Raz has been good and quiet all morning," said Mrs. Moon with a puzzled look on her face. "Do you think he's sick?"

Alan laughed, "I know why he's not barking and misbehaving. He recalls our big dinner last night and is hoping to get leftovers."

"Nonsense," said Mrs. Moon, smiling. "Raz doesn't remember that there are leftovers. Sometimes he doesn't even remember his own name when we call him. Well, let's feed him anyway."

After Raz had finished eating the leftovers, he began barking and acting up like his old self.

---

4.   Mr. Perez stood in front of the well-stocked rack, looking at magazines. He paged through several and then put them back.

Mr. Corbett, the owner of the store, said, "Hey, are you going to buy magazines, or are you just going to stand there and read them? Tell me, would you like a chair?"

Mr. Perez stared angrily at Mr. Corbett. "I was trying to decide which magazines to buy." Mr. Perez' face grew red with rage. "Mr. Corbett, I've spent plenty of money in your store through the years, but I have made my last purchase here."

---

5.   "Did everybody do the homework last night?" asked Mr. Montez.

"Yes," answered all the students.

"Then, Sally, perhaps you can answer the first question."

"I didn't understand the question," said Sally. "I didn't know how to answer it."

"Did you answer the second question?" asked Mr. Montez.

Sally shook her head.

"In that case, you didn't do the homework," said Mr. Montez. "I only assigned two questions."

UNIT 16

		T	F	I
1.	(A) Mrs. Cramer suggested that Jennifer sit on the porch.	☐	☐	☐
	(B) Matt maintains an unfailing practice schedule.	☐	☐	☐
	(C) Jennifer planned to attend a party at three.	☐	☐	☐
	(D) Mrs. Cramer hears Matt's playing from the porch.	☐	☐	☐

		T	F	I
2.	(A) Nicole had trouble sleeping because she had mistreated her friend.	☐	☐	☐
	(B) Nicole apologized to Lorraine for losing her temper.	☐	☐	☐
	(C) Lorraine doesn't hold grudges.	☐	☐	☐
	(D) Nicole waited until after school was over to apologize to Lorraine.	☐	☐	☐

		T	F	I
3.	(A) Raz is not always a good dog.	☐	☐	☐
	(B) Alan said he knew why Raz wasn't barking and misbehaving.	☐	☐	☐
	(C) Mrs. Moon wondered if Raz might be sick.	☐	☐	☐
	(D) Raz did not eat the leftovers.	☐	☐	☐

		T	F	I
4.	(A) Mr. Perez would advise his friends not to patronize Mr. Corbett's store.	☐	☐	☐
	(B) Mr. Corbett's remarks angered Mr. Perez.	☐	☐	☐
	(C) Mr. Corbett's magazine store was poorly stocked.	☐	☐	☐
	(D) Mr. Perez would storm out of the store without buying anything.	☐	☐	☐

		T	F	I
5.	(A) Sally didn't want to admit that she hadn't done the assignment.	☐	☐	☐
	(B) All the children in the class said they had done their homework.	☐	☐	☐
	(C) Finally, Mr. Montez told Sally that she hadn't done her homework.	☐	☐	☐
	(D) Sally was lying when she said she didn't understand the question.	☐	☐	☐

1. "I've known Bill for years, but I've never seen him so upset," said Tom, looking unhappily at Carlos across the table. "He didn't even finish his hamburger."

"Try to forget it," said Carlos consolingly. "You know Bill. He has a hot temper, but he cools off quickly."

"Just the same, I think I'll apologize." And he scrambled out of his chair and took off in hot pursuit of his friend.

---

2. Propped up against the bed pillows, Benito stared thoughtfully at the playing cards in his hand. "Which one should I discard?" he mumbled, fingering one card, then another.

"Come on," said his friend Mickey, sitting cross-legged at the end of the bed. "Just because you're sick doesn't mean you can take all day."

"But I want to make sure I pick the right one," insisted Benito.

"That will be the day," replied Mickey.

---

3. Standing in the doorway of his sister's room, Sam looked distastefully at the clutter. "When are you going to clean up this mess?" he asked.

Maria, sitting in the center of the floor amid scattered magazines, stared at her brother in mock outrage. "How can you say that?" she said. "My room is a model of efficiency."

Sam refused to be put off. "I don't see how you can find anything," he persisted. "This place looks like a disaster area."

"To each his own," replied Maria.

---

4. Peter Wong remained outwardly calm. But inside he was bubbling with excitement. "I can't believe we're finally on our way!" he said to his brother, gazing with wonder at the strange countryside whizzing past the train window.

Lin Wong was young enough to be unembarrassed by displays of emotion. His small face was radiant.

"Just think," he chattered. "We'll get to eat in a good restaurant, and we'll each have a bedroom!"

---

5. Maya had wanted a dog of her own for a long time. Now that her family had moved to a new house with a small backyard, she had finally gotten her wish. Her parents had given her a delightful black puppy.

"Have you thought of a name yet, Maya?" asked her friend Francesca.

"Not yet," answered Maya. "Nothing seems just right."

It didn't take long before Maya knew what to name her puppy.

"Your name has to be Digger!" shrieked Maya, as she looked at her mother's flower garden.

UNIT 17

		T	F	I
1.	(A) Bill didn't finish eating his hamburger.	☐	☐	☐
	(B) Tom had known Bill for a long time.	☐	☐	☐
	(C) Tom left to apologize to Bill.	☐	☐	☐
	(D) Bill will not be upset with Tom for long.	☐	☐	☐

		T	F	I
2.	(A) Mickey was sick in bed.	☐	☐	☐
	(B) Mickey does not consider Benito to be a good card player.	☐	☐	☐
	(C) Mickey sat at the end of the bed with his legs crossed.	☐	☐	☐
	(D) Benito finds it hard to make decisions.	☐	☐	☐

		T	F	I
3.	(A) Sam told Maria her room was a mess.	☐	☐	☐
	(B) The magazines were stacked neatly in a corner.	☐	☐	☐
	(C) Maria didn't let Sam's remarks bother her.	☐	☐	☐
	(D) Maria was asleep when Sam looked in her room.	☐	☐	☐

		T	F	I
4.	(A) Lin and Peter Wong saw unfamiliar scenery.	☐	☐	☐
	(B) The brothers will be having new experiences.	☐	☐	☐
	(C) Both boys were excited about the trip.	☐	☐	☐
	(D) Lin is Peter's older brother.	☐	☐	☐

		T	F	I
5.	(A) Maya's puppy has destroyed the flower garden.	☐	☐	☐
	(B) Francesca thought of the name for Maya's puppy.	☐	☐	☐
	(C) The dog was a gift to Maya.	☐	☐	☐
	(D) Maya's puppy had brown and white spots.	☐	☐	☐

1.   Lihwa was surprised to find a large silver key lying next to her favorite sitting-rock in the woods. When she held the key, it spoke to her. "Use me, Lihwa, to open the All-Time-Door."

Lihwa looked around and saw a large wooden door in the side of a huge oak tree. She slipped the silver key into the lock, and the huge door opened. . . .

---

2.   "My school grades were fine until I took this part-time job," moaned Fred. "Every other term I earned A's and B's. Now I'm getting mostly C's."

"But my grades went down too," Beth pointed out, "and I don't have a job. Everyone's grades have dropped since Ms. Meehan took over the class from Mr. Sweet."

---

3.   "You can tell how much snow fell in these woods last winter by looking at the pine trees," said Mr. Winkler. "Notice that all the needles are nibbled off the pines from about three feet above the ground to about eight feet. Deer have eaten those needles."

"I see," said Liz. "The bare parts of the branches show how low and how high the deer have nibbled off the needles."

---

4.   "I've got some bad news," Herb solemnly told his mother and father. "The clock in the hall doesn't work anymore."

"It was working fine earlier," said Mother. "What happened?"

"Well," said Herb as he shifted from one foot to the other, "it doesn't work now because it's in pieces."

"In pieces?" said Father anxiously. "Did it fall off the shelf?"

"Not exactly," said Herb, his voice quivering. He hung his head and stared at the floor. "I took it apart because I wanted to see how it worked . . . and now I can't get it back together again."

---

5.   "Look at the big red apple I found under the tree in my backyard," said Marty.

"Could I take a closer look at that apple?" asked Pam.

"Certainly," said Marty.

Pam looked carefully at the apple. "I don't think you want to eat this apple," she ascertained.

"Oh, and why is that?" asked Marty.

"See the tiny holes?" asked Pam. "Do you know what made them?"

"No," said Marty, taking the apple back and biting into it.

25 Jan 05

			T	F	I
1.	(A)	Lihwa was unable to unlock the door in the tree with the key.	☐	☐	☐
	(B)	Lihwa believed in magical happenings.	☐	☐	☐
	(C)	Lihwa was adventurous.	☐	☐	☐
	(D)	Lihwa had not expected to find the key.	☐	☐	☐

			T	F	I
2.	(A)	Fred said his school grades now were mostly C's.	☐	☐	☐
	(B)	Beth's grades were higher this term.	☐	☐	☐
	(C)	Ms. Meehan is a stricter marker than Mr. Sweet.	☐	☐	☐
	(D)	Fred had previously been a straight-A student.	☐	☐	☐

			T	F	I
3.	(A)	Mr. Winkler explained that deer had eaten the pine needles.	☐	☐	☐
	(B)	There had been three feet of snow last winter.	☐	☐	☐
	(C)	Deer had eaten all the needles on the pine trees.	☐	☐	☐
	(D)	Deer can't reach the needles that are over eight feet high.	☐	☐	☐

			T	F	I
4.	(A)	Herb told his parents that he had good news.	☐	☐	☐
	(B)	Father asked if the clock had fallen off the shelf.	☐	☐	☐
	(C)	Herb felt upset and guilty.	☐	☐	☐
	(D)	Herb had taken the clock apart.	☐	☐	☐

			T	F	I
5.	(A)	Marty ate some worms along with the apple.	☐	☐	☐
	(B)	Pam showed Marty the holes in the apple.	☐	☐	☐
	(C)	Marty found the apple in his own backyard.	☐	☐	☐
	(D)	Pam found the apple to be in perfect condition.	☐	☐	☐

1.　"I don't want to see another horror movie," said Marge. "After the last one I saw, I had bad dreams for a week."

"Oh, come on!" said Chuck. "You can't really be afraid of something you know isn't real."

Marge turned away and took a gruesome-looking mask of a werewolf from under her coat. Then she put it over her face. When she turned to face Chuck, he let out a hair-raising scream of panic.

"Now do you understand why I don't like horror movies?" asked Marge calmly.

2.　"I can't seem to get to sleep," said Tina. "I just keep tossing and turning when I'm in bed. I keep thinking of all the exciting things I could be doing instead of sleeping."

"I've got an answer," said Father. "I'm going to read you a book."

Father came into Tina's room with a book.

"Oh, no, not that book!" said Tina. "That's the most boring book in the world."

"I know," said Father. Then he began to read. Soon Tina was sound asleep.

3.　"Weren't there Japanese knights that were something like the knights in Europe during the Middle Ages?" asked Rickie.

"Yes," replied Aunt Elise. "They were called Samurai. Their goal in life was to protect their lords. To do this, Samurai knights became very skilled with swords and bows and arrows. Like European knights, Samurai knights lived by a strict code of bravery, self-control, and loyalty," explained Aunt Elise.

4.　"What's your name, and why are you crying?" Lynn asked the little boy.

"My name is Rob, and I'm crying because I'm lost," he said. "There are so many people in this big store. I can't find my mother."

Suddenly the little boy began to smile. "There she is!" he shouted. Rob's mother had spotted her little son and was moving toward him. The little boy was very happy to see his mother.

"From now on," said Rob's mother, "you'd better hold my hand when we're in the store."

5.　"I caught a garter snake!" yelled Cathy, as she ran up to her friend, Tim.

"That's great. I've never seen a snake that wasn't in a cage," said Tim.

"Well," said Cathy, "I have one right here in this box."

Cathy set the box down on the ground and opened it. There was absolutely nothing inside.

"So where's this garter snake of yours?" asked Tim expectantly.

Then Cathy noticed a little hole in the corner of the box.

UNIT 19

			T	F	I
1.	(A)	Marge knew beforehand that Chuck would try to make her see the horror movie.	☐	☐	☐
	(B)	Chuck enjoyed watching scary movies.	☐	☐	☐
	(C)	Marge took the werewolf mask from under her coat.	☐	☐	☐
	(D)	Chuck thought the werewolf mask was funny.	☐	☐	☐

			T	F	I
2.	(A)	Tina said that Father had chosen the most boring book in the world.	☐	☐	☐
	(B)	Tina went to sleep because the book didn't interest her.	☐	☐	☐
	(C)	Tina was happy about the book Father was going to read.	☐	☐	☐
	(D)	Father's answer to the problem didn't work.	☐	☐	☐

			T	F	I
3.	(A)	Samurai knights practiced swordsmanship and archery.	☐	☐	☐
	(B)	To a Samurai, the most important person in the world was his lord.	☐	☐	☐
	(C)	Samurai often risked their lives for their lords.	☐	☐	☐
	(D)	Knights like the Samurai existed only in Japan.	☐	☐	☐

			T	F	I
4.	(A)	The little boy's mother was thankful to find her son.	☐	☐	☐
	(B)	The boy hadn't been holding his mother's hand before he became lost.	☐	☐	☐
	(C)	Lynn asked the little boy why he was crying.	☐	☐	☐
	(D)	The little boy was sad to see his mother.	☐	☐	☐

			T	F	I
5.	(A)	Tim had seen snakes before, but they had been in cages.	☐	☐	☐
	(B)	Cathy said the snake she had caught was in the box.	☐	☐	☐
	(C)	The snake had escaped from the box through the little hole.	☐	☐	☐
	(D)	Cathy had a let-down feeling when she realized what had happened.	☐	☐	☐

"I don't want to see another horror movie," said Marge. "After the last one I saw, I had bad dreams for a week."

"Oh, come on!" said Chuck. "You can't really be afraid of something you know isn't real."

Marge turned away and took a gruesome-looking mask of a werewolf from under her coat. Then she put it over her face. When she turned to face Chuck, he let out a hair-raising scream of panic.

"Now do you understand why I don't like horror movies?" asked Marge calmly.

A. Exercising Your Skill

In the passage above, you can guess that the movie frightened Marge so much that she had bad dreams for a week. You can guess that Chuck was probably frightened by the werewolf mask because he let out a hair-raising scream. In stories, characters act in certain ways when they have certain feelings, such as fear, anger, excitement, or boredom. Sometimes characters' feelings are described directly in a story. Other times you can guess what they are probably feeling because of what they do or because of what they say in dialogue, or conversation.

The list below tells things a person did. For each action on the list, tell what emotion the character was probably feeling, such as fear, anger, excitement, or boredom. If the behavior could suggest more than one feeling, say so.

Actions:
- frowned deeply
- chuckled quietly
- started to tremble all over
- gasped, "Wow!"
- let out a piercing wail
- felt eyelids sink like weights
- clenched fists
- yawned repeatedly
- broke out in a cold sweat
- jumped at every noise
- gritted teeth
- felt eyes open wide
- jumped up and down and clapped hands
- sat straight up in bed

B. Expanding Your Skill

For one emotion, such as surprise or grief, write several character actions like the ones above. Read your actions to a partner. Can your partner guess which emotion the actions express?

C. Exploring Language

Write and illustrate a short fantasy story book for young children. Decide on two characters—such as a big, friendly dragon named Donald and a light-as-a-feather sprite named Sophie. Make up a simple plot that will involve the characters in situations that can bring forth two or three emotions. Plan to reveal these emotions—such as joy, wonder, fear, and excitement—through the characters' actions and conversations rather than by describing them directly.

Illustrate each page of the book and include three to five lines of story text on each page.

You may want to organize the information for your book in this way:

1. Characters: _____
2. Setting: _____
3. Problem: _____
   • Action: _____
   • Action: _____
   • Action: _____
4. Resolution: _____

5. Emotions Revealed by
   Actions and Conversations:
   _____
   _____
   _____
   _____
   _____

Ask one or two classmates to read your story and to identify the emotions revealed by actions and conversations. Then give the book to a young child to read and enjoy!

D. Expressing Yourself

Choose one of these activities.

1. Pretend that you are a television reporter on the site of an exciting sports event—and history is in the making. You are on the air live and telling your audience what is happening as it happens. Try to capture the feelings of the participants and the spectators by revealing their actions, rather than by describing the feelings directly. For example: "The crowd is hushed. Leah stands at the tape, reaches high over her head, and slams the ball into Nina's fair-play area. Leah lets out a whoop as she wins the set, the match, and the game!" Present your broadcast to your classmates, and see if they "catch" the mood.

2. Make up sayings for fortune cookies. Write sayings that link behavior with feelings. For example: "A smile on your face speaks louder than words." "One who wastes time can never feel thrifty at heart." You and your classmates may want to throw your sayings into a hat and then each pick a fortune for the day.

1.   Rover was lying comfortably at Mrs. McIntosh's feet as she knitted in her chair. Suddenly the dog lifted its head, raised its ears, and let out a low growl.

"Easy, Rover," said Mrs. McIntosh. "I thought I heard something outside, too. But we're safe here in our living room. If anyone tries to break in, the police will know and be here within two minutes."

---

2.   "I just read about a certain type of tree that has roots that grow downward from its branches and then take root in the soil below," said Seiji.

"Really?" Kin responded. "What kind of tree is that, and where does it grow?"

"It's the banyan tree, and it grows in India," said Seiji. "I also read that sometimes there are so many roots growing down that one banyan tree can look like an entire grove!"

---

3.   "I'm not afraid of this old house, even at night," boasted Nancy.

"You haven't heard then," said Shirley, "of a private graveyard behind the house. The ghost of a vicious dog haunts the property."

"Oh, come on . . . " said Nancy. "I don't believe that for a second."

"See those claw scratches on the door?" asked Shirley. "They were left by the ghost dog after it chased the former owner through the yard. That's why no one will buy the house now."

"Let's get out of here," Nancy said suddenly.

"Why are you in such a hurry to leave?" asked Shirley.

---

4.   Atop the snow-covered mountain, the sign pointing to the left said "Beginner's Trail." Leslie adjusted her ski bindings and gazed down the left trail. It dropped off very steeply, and she could see several sharp, narrow turns. "Something's wrong here," she thought. "This can't be a beginner's trail. The trail to the right looks easier to me. I wonder if those snickering youngsters I saw walking away from the signpost had anything to do with this."

---

5.   "I'm sorry," said the telephone operator, "but the number you have reached has been temporarily disconnected."

"But that's my own phone number!" shouted Jerry.

"I'm sorry," the voice repeated, "but the number you have rea . . . "

"Ugh," moaned Jerry, "a recorded message. Well, I'm going home to see why my phone isn't working."

When Jerry got to his street, he saw a telephone repair truck and a police car there. A car had knocked down a telephone pole.

"When will my phone be fixed?" Jerry demanded of the workers.

"We'll have it working again within a half hour," they answe a Feb. 05

		T	F	I
1.	(A) Rover is a good watchdog.	☐	☐	☐
	(B) Mrs. McIntosh's home is equipped with a burglar alarm.	☐	☐	☐
	(C) Mrs. McIntosh did not feel safe in the living room.	☐	☐	☐
	(D) Mrs. McIntosh said the police could arrive within two minutes.	☐	☐	☐

		T	F	I
2.	(A) Seiji learned about banyan trees from a movie.	☐	☐	☐
	(B) A banyan tree can look like a grove.	☐	☐	☐
	(C) Banyan tree roots grow from the branches down to the soil.	☐	☐	☐
	(D) Seiji and Kin do not live in India.	☐	☐	☐

		T	F	I
3.	(A) At first, Nancy didn't believe Shirley's story.	☐	☐	☐
	(B) Nancy boasted about not being afraid of the old house.	☐	☐	☐
	(C) Shirley made up the story to frighten Nancy.	☐	☐	☐
	(D) Shirley said, "Let's get out of here."	☐	☐	☐

		T	F	I
4.	(A) The left trail was steep and sharply curved.	☐	☐	☐
	(B) Leslie didn't detect any difference between the beginner's and the advanced trails.	☐	☐	☐
	(C) The youngsters had put the "Beginner's Trail" sign at the entrance to the advanced trail.	☐	☐	☐
	(D) Leslie didn't go down the left trail.	☐	☐	☐

		T	F	I
5.	(A) Jerry was shouting at a recording, not a live operator.	☐	☐	☐
	(B) The repairers said Jerry's phone would be working again in fifteen minutes.	☐	☐	☐
	(C) Jerry does not have much patience.	☐	☐	☐
	(D) A telephone pole had been knocked down.	☐	☐	☐

1.   "Hey, Jill, wake up," whispered Tricia as she elbowed her friend gently.

"Uh . . . oh," mumbled Jill. "I hardly sleep at night. Mom and Dad get up for the feedings, but I just can't resist peeking at Josh every time I hear him wake up."

"Girls, do you have something to share with us?" asked Mr. Rizzo, at the board.

---

2.   Painters have often been able to correct a mistake with one or more brush strokes. Bette Clair Nesmith had long watched with fascination as her artist friends would paint over an error and start again. This gave Nesmith, an executive secretary, an idea. She decided to do the same thing at her office. Using a tempera water-base paint and a small brush, Nesmith began to cover her typing errors. The new product she created—correction fluid—has since become an indispensable tool in most offices and many homes.

---

3.   A legend of the French and Indian War tells of a little Pennsylvania Dutch girl named Regina, who was taken captive by the Indians. Later, when she and other captive girls and women were freed, a Colonel Bouquet put them up in a line on a square in Carlisle, Pennsylvania. Regina's mother went to the square hoping to find her child but recognized no one in the line. Then the mother began to sing an old hymn that she and her daughter had often sung together years ago. A young woman stepped out of the line and began singing along.

---

4.   It takes fifteen to eighteen years for a human's bones, which consist mainly of calcium and phosphorus, to grow and for the person to reach full height. In four to five months, a male deer's antlers, which are bony outgrowths, are complete. The antlers begin as small bumps on the frontal bones of the deer's skull. The skin, or velvet, that covers these bumps grows along with them. In late summer, when the antlers have stopped growing, the velvet dries up and falls off. At the end of the spring mating season, the antlers are shed and the deer grows a new set. Biologists know of no faster bone growth than that of antlers.

---

5.   People who cry are healthier than people who suppress their tears, according to at least two university professors who have made special studies. Emotional tears shed during stressful or sad times can relieve tension and even prevent such bodily disturbances as ulcers or colitis. People actually look better after a good cry. Less irritation is apparent in their faces. Said Professor Scheff of the University of Santa Barbara, "Afterwards there are no bagging under the eyes, no bloodshot eyes, no headaches."

UNIT 21

17 Feb 05

		T	F	I

1. (A) Jill and Tricia are in school.
    (B) Josh is Jill's baby brother.
    (C) Jill's mother and father share the feeding of Josh.
    (D) Jill can sleep through any kind of disturbance.

2. (A) Correction fluid is used in most offices and many homes.
    (B) A painter can often paint over an error and start again.
    (C) Nesmith's invention is useful to students.
    (D) Nesmith made a good deal of money from her idea.

3. (A) Regina was taken captive by Indians during the French and Indian War.
    (B) The young woman who stepped out of line and began singing the hymn was Regina.
    (C) Regina's mother recognized her daughter on sight.
    (D) Colonel Bouquet put the freed women in a line on the square in Carlisle, Pennsylvania.

4. (A) The antlers of a male deer grow to full size in four to five months.
    (B) The antlers of a deer contain the same substances found in the bones of humans.
    (C) It takes fifteen to eighteen years for a person to reach full height.
    (D) The antlers of a deer usually begin growing in late summer.

5. (A) University professors have made special studies of people who cry.
    (B) People who pretend to cry (crocodile tears) may not gain the benefits of tension relief.
    (C) After people cry, they show less irritation in their faces.
    (D) Ulcers are caused by too much crying.

1. Is a single vote important? President Thomas Jefferson was elected by only one vote in the House of Representatives. So was President John Quincy Adams. Rutherford B. Hayes won the Presidency by a single electoral vote. Likewise, Texas, Oregon, Washington, and Idaho were admitted into the United States by one Senatorial vote each. In 1941, just before the U.S. involvement in World War II, Congress ruled—again by a single vote—to continue the Selective Service Act, drafting men into the army to keep America prepared.

2. Lindsay had been at camp for three weeks. Her favorite activity was canoeing. When the day came for her to take her canoe test, Lindsay felt confident that she would pass. She knew the strokes and could steer a canoe well. The counselor who was testing Lindsay sat in the middle of the canoe; Lindsay was in the stern. The trip started out well with Lindsay paddling strongly and in full control. But suddenly, while switching her paddle from one side to the other, Lindsay lost her grip on it. The paddle slipped and hit the counselor on the head!

3. Cousins Ranelle Holley and Gilbert Deans joined their parents on an outing to White Sands National Monument in New Mexico. The cousins soon kicked off their shoes to play in nature's huge "sandbox."

"White Sands covers 275 square miles," said Mrs. Deans to her sister, Mrs. Holley. "The dunes are composed of gypsum, a mineral used to make plaster of Paris. What an interesting place this is!"

While the sisters chatted, Mr. Deans and Mr. Holley asked the children to race up a steep dune with them. The cousins quickly made it to the top. The fathers were only partway up when the delighted children rolled down past them at lightning speed!

4. In the forty years they were married, Mrs. Tracey and her husband had run the family business and reared their seven children. When her husband died, Mrs. Tracey continued to stay on in the big house, even though the children were out living on their own. It was nice having a large house when the grandchildren came to visit. Mrs. Tracey enjoyed her garden of flowers and vegetables and enjoyed having her friends in for tea. But now she was ninety and finding it harder and harder to keep the big house going or even to cook and care for herself. She had to make plans to change her way of life.

5. The great-granddaughter of Louis Wilson made the following notes: "According to the deed, Louis Wilson purchased a farm in Centerville in 1872. This was a 160-acre parcel. He married Ruth Sanders in 1877."

"Other relatives living in this area included Charles Wilson, the general contractor. In 1880 he built the courthouse."

"A Lucy Wilson also made rural land purchases here in 1883 and 1884, and a Lucy Wilson who died in 1910 is buried in the church cemetery in Centerville."

UNIT 22

1.
		T	F	I
(A)	One person's political opinion can change history.	☐	☐	☐
(B)	Idaho was admitted into the United States by one Senatorial vote.	☐	☐	☐
(C)	Jefferson, Adams, and Washington were elected President by a single vote each.	☐	☐	☐
(D)	An eligible voter cannot afford to abstain from voting on Election Day.	☐	☐	☐

2.
		T	F	I
(A)	Lindsay didn't pass her canoe test that day.	☐	☐	☐
(B)	The counselor sat in the middle of the canoe.	☐	☐	☐
(C)	Lindsay knew beforehand that she'd never pass the test.	☐	☐	☐
(D)	After the paddle slipped, Lindsay was very embarrassed.	☐	☐	☐

3.
		T	F	I
(A)	White Sands National Monument covers 275 square miles.	☐	☐	☐
(B)	The cousins had the most fun on the outing.	☐	☐	☐
(C)	Mrs. Holley and Mrs. Deans are sisters.	☐	☐	☐
(D)	Plaster of Paris is made from gypsum.	☐	☐	☐

4.
		T	F	I
(A)	Mr. Tracey outlived Mrs. Tracey.	☐	☐	☐
(B)	Mrs. Tracey has decided to sell the big house.	☐	☐	☐
(C)	The Traceys had been married for forty years.	☐	☐	☐
(D)	Mrs. Tracey was thinking about entering a senior-citizen residence.	☐	☐	☐

5.
		T	F	I
(A)	The great-granddaughter of Louis Wilson was making notes for a family tree.	☐	☐	☐
(B)	Ruth Sanders married Charles Wilson.	☐	☐	☐
(C)	The courthouse was built in 1880.	☐	☐	☐
(D)	The notes would have to be correlated with other research on the Wilsons.	☐	☐	☐

1.   Professor Richard Eakin of the University of California enlivened his biology classes by impersonating famous scientists. When the renowned nineteenth-century biologist Charles Darwin was the subject, Professor Eakin would don a false beard and a frock coat and "guest-lecture" as Darwin himself might have done. To teach the findings of the priest-scientist Gregor Mendel, Eakin would appear in clerical robes. He also imitated the appearance and accent of Louis Pasteur. Eakin would spend up to three hours applying makeup for a role. He found that a scientific idea meant more to his students when the discoverer himself seemed to be explaining it.

2.   From 1929 to 1941 a steam-powered train, the *Blue Comet*, offered luxury runs between New York City and Atlantic City, New Jersey. The interior and exterior of the train were mostly blue. The blue of the exterior was broken by a cream-colored stripe that ran the length of the train on both sides. The *Blue Comet* provided fast, three-hour service between the two cities. People used to line the tracks just to watch the train fly by. Everything about it suggested a speeding blue comet. Each car of the train was even named for a celestial comet. The *Blue Comet* made its final trip on September 27, 1941.

3.   Jenny and her father had flown to the West Indies and were vacationing on the beach in Jamaica there.
    "Dad, you were in the naval submarine service," said Jenny. "What is it really like to travel in a submarine?"
    "I can do better than describe what it's like," said Dad. "Believe it or not, I've arranged for the two of us to explore the undersea world around Grand Cayman tomorrow. We'll be leaving early on a twenty-eight-passenger submarine named the *Atlantis*. Now you'll finally be able to see for yourself how exciting submarine travel really is."

4.   Eleven-year-old Stacie Lee Walker of Kennesaw, Georgia, wrote an essay for a mother-of-the-year contest. But since her parents are divorced, and she lives with her father, Stacie described her dad as "the best Mom that's really a Dad." Her essay was chosen as the winning one from more than 750 entries. Another interesting sentence in her essay was, "I know my Dad is not my Mom, but he's been like a mother to me." Stacie's father, Robert J. Walker, who is an electronics mechanic, was surprised and pleased to be named "Mom of the Year."

5.   Humankind sometimes experiences terrible tragedies, then realizes that preventive safety measures could have saved countless lives. Ever since the great loss of life that resulted when the *Titanic* sank in 1912, ships must carry sufficient lifeboats and operate their radios twenty-four hours a day. Because 168 people were killed in a circus-tent fire in Hartford, Connecticut, in 1944, modern circus tents are made of nonflammable materials. In 1986, the loss of life on U.S. shuttle mission 51-L and at the Chernobyl nuclear plant in the Soviet Union alerted the world to the fact that safety can never be taken for granted.

			T	F	I
1.	(A)	Professor Eakin taught biology in California.	□	□	□
	(B)	Professor Eakin usually dressed as a clown for his lectures.	□	□	□
	(C)	Professor Eakin was a good actor.	□	□	□
	(D)	Professor Eakin enjoyed teaching.	□	□	□

			T	F	I
2.	(A)	It took three hours to travel from New York City to Atlantic City on the *Blue Comet*.	□	□	□
	(B)	Passengers aboard the *Blue Comet* received exceptionally fine service.	□	□	□
	(C)	The *Blue Comet* was a diesel-powered train.	□	□	□
	(D)	The seats and the carpeting of the train were mostly blue.	□	□	□

			T	F	I
3.	(A)	Jenny's father had arranged a trip on the *Nautilus*.	□	□	□
	(B)	Jamaica is in the West Indies.	□	□	□
	(C)	Jenny has heard tales about the exciting life aboard a submarine.	□	□	□
	(D)	Jenny's father enjoyed his submarine duty of the past.	□	□	□

			T	F	I
4.	(A)	Stacie and her father get along well together.	□	□	□
	(B)	Robert Walker and his wife are divorced.	□	□	□
	(C)	Stacie's father spends as much time as possible with Stacie.	□	□	□
	(D)	Stacie's essay was the only entry in the contest.	□	□	□

			T	F	I
5.	(A)	The *Titanic* was not equipped with enough lifeboats for all its passengers.	□	□	□
	(B)	Two major disasters in 1986 occurred in the United States and in the Soviet Union.	□	□	□
	(C)	A circus-tent fire in Hartford, Connecticut, killed 168 people.	□	□	□
	(D)	Important knowledge is acquired as the result of tragedies.	□	□	□

1.   The largest and heaviest horses in the world are the great shires, weighing over two thousand pounds and standing as high as eighteen hands (six feet) at the shoulder. The shires can haul heavy loads. Two shires in England pulled a world-record load for horses: fifty-six tons.

In the Middle Ages, when English knights were seeking a breed of horse that would carry an armored warrior into battle, they chose the shire. In fact, the horses themselves wore armor from head to hoof.

Modern horse lovers call shires "the gentle giants."

---

2.   "The opposing team is desperate to win," remarked Pat. "They'll do anything, even sneak in a ringer."

"What's a ringer?" asked Ron.

"A top-notch player that a team brings in from outside but who's not officially allowed to be on the team. Some teams try to get away with using a ringer, but it's illegal," replied Pat.

Just then Ron looked at the opposing team's bench and saw a huge player, over six feet tall and muscular, almost bursting out of the uniform. "I've never seen that one before," said Ron. "I wonder. . . ."

---

3.   Are you accustomed to entering your house through a door in the roof? You probably aren't, but the early Pueblo Indians were. For protection, the windows of their multi-storied brick dwellings were located high off the ground. Likewise, the doors were located in the roofs and could be reached only by way of removable ladders. Thus, Pueblo Indians often "came down the door."

---

4.   In Texas City, Texas, on April 15, 1947, firefighters were trying to put out a smoky blaze aboard the docked French freighter *Grandcamp*. They couldn't use much water because it would damage the cargo. Fourteen hundred tons of that cargo was explosive ammonium nitrate.

Realizing the danger, port officials ordered the *Grandcamp* towed to sea. Too late! A sudden explosion wiped out ship, dock, firefighters, and onlookers. Chain-reaction blasts devastated most of Texas City. Officials counted 468 dead; others say the toll was 1,000. The tragedy was likely caused by a careless smoker on the *Grandcamp*.

---

5.   The creature that South American jungle dwellers fear most is the anaconda, a green-and-black snake that can swallow deer—whole.

Anacondas are the largest of the boa family snakes. Determining how long they can grow involves untangling fact from legend. Explorers have claimed seeing forty-, sixty-, and even 140-foot anacondas. The "official" record—s i not universally accepted—is $37\frac{1}{2}$ feet. A $5,000 prize offered for a thirty-footer has never been claimed. But twenty-footers are common. The anaconda kills by suffocating its prey.

UNIT 24

			T	F	I
1.	(A)	Shires were used as war horses during the Middle Ages.	☐	☐	☐
	(B)	Two shires in England pulled fifty-six tons.	☐	☐	☐
	(C)	Knights would try to kill an enemy knight's horse.	☐	☐	☐
	(D)	Shires could not bear the weight of heavy armor.	☐	☐	☐

			T	F	I
2.	(A)	The huge player was a ringer.	☐	☐	☐
	(B)	The opposing team was cheating.	☐	☐	☐
	(C)	Pat learned what a ringer is from Ron.	☐	☐	☐
	(D)	As a general rule, teams are permitted to use ringers.	☐	☐	☐

			T	F	I
3.	(A)	Early Pueblo Indians lived in wooden frame houses.	☐	☐	☐
	(B)	The dwellings of the Pueblos often had more than one level.	☐	☐	☐
	(C)	The Pueblos had enemies nearby.	☐	☐	☐
	(D)	Pueblo dwellings had roof-level doors.	☐	☐	☐

			T	F	I
4.	(A)	The explosion occurred in 1947.	☐	☐	☐
	(B)	Spraying too much water on the fire would have damaged the cargo.	☐	☐	☐
	(C)	Someone put the value of goods above the value of lives.	☐	☐	☐
	(D)	Most of Texas City was destroyed by chain-reaction blasts.	☐	☐	☐

			T	F	I
5.	(A)	The anaconda is not a poisonous snake.	☐	☐	☐
	(B)	The anaconda is the smallest member of the boa family.	☐	☐	☐
	(C)	Jungle dwellers fear the anaconda more than any other creature.	☐	☐	☐
	(D)	The anaconda kills by suffocating its victim.	☐	☐	☐

1.   Sergei looked forward to his first meal with his American family. An exchange student from the Ukraine, Sergei would be spending three months in the United States, learning about the country's people and their culture. At dinner Sergei was bombarded with questions from the Johnsons, especially from Michelle, the talkative eight-year-old.

Her first question, "What is your family like?" was followed in quick succession by "Do you have a sister my age?" and "Is the weather cold in the Ukraine?" and so on.

"Hey, Michelle," interrupted Craig, her older brother. "Maybe Sergei would like to get a question in sometime soon?"

---

2.   Reatha hopped off the bus at State Street and dashed into the department store. In a moment she found the electronics department. "Here," she showed the clerk the newspaper ad. "I want one of the lightweight earphone radios you have on sale for $15. The ad says the sale ends today."

With an expression of surprise, the clerk took the ad and read it. Then, with a snicker, the clerk called over another clerk and read the ad. "This kid wants one of *our* $15 radios!" Both clerks laughed out loud.

---

3.   "Something's all wrong," muttered Rachel as she opened her eyes to the bright morning sun streaming through her bedroom window. "The sun shouldn't be up. It's the middle of January, and my electric alarm clock says 6:30 A.M. It should still be dark outside."

Rachel checked the clock. The numbers were lit, and the digits changed to 6:31 as she watched. The clock definitely was working. But from the avenue she heard sounds of school buses, which normally don't run until after eight.

---

4.   Grayson broke away from the defender and dribbled in for another easy score. The home-team crowd groaned. The home team was now down by seven points with two minutes to go.

In the stands, the home crowd wondered why Coach Browne hadn't put Horgan in. Horgan not only was the team's high scorer but was at least two inches taller than anyone on the opposing team.

Finally, the coach motioned for Horgan to go in. The crowd cheered wildly. Horgan jumped up and trotted onto the court, limping. The crowd suddenly quieted.

---

5.   The landlord unlocked the vacant apartment, and the young couple stepped inside the empty rooms. The apartment was not in a very safe neighborhood, but it was the only one they had seen so far that they could afford.

"Clean and neat," said the landlord, grinning. "A little paint and it'll look like it belongs on Park Avenue."

The couple examined the kitchen. "Why are these little boxes of pellets marked 'poison' behind the refrigerator and the stove?" asked the young woman.

UNIT 25

T F I

1. (A) The Johnsons were hosting an exchange student from the Ukraine.
    (B) Sergei had arrived at the Johnsons' home three weeks ago.
    (C) Craig thought Michelle was being overly nosey and rude.
    (D) Michelle was only eight years old.

T F I

2. (A) Reatha got off the bus at State Street.
    (B) Reatha went to the electronics department of the store.
    (C) Reatha wanted to buy a radio that was on sale.
    (D) Reatha had gone to the wrong store.

T F I

3. (A) When Rachel awoke, her clock indicated that it was 6:30 A.M.
    (B) Rachel will be late for school.
    (C) The electric power had gone off during the night.
    (D) It was a cloudy day.

T F I

4. (A) The home team was at a disadvantage without Horgan.
    (B) Grayson was on the home team.
    (C) Horgan was the team's high scorer.
    (D) The coach had kept Horgan out because of an injury.

T F I

5. (A) Park Avenue is known for its fine residences.
    (B) The apartment was troubled by mice or rats.
    (C) The apartment was furnished.
    (D) The couple could afford the apartment.

A legend of the French and Indian War tells of a little Pennsylvania Dutch girl named Regina, who was taken captive by the Indians. Later, when she and other captive girls and women were freed, a Colonel Bouquet put them up in a line on a square in Carlisle, Pennsylvania. Regina's mother went to the square hoping to find her child but recognized no one in the line. Then the mother began to sing an old hymn that she and her daughter had often sung together years ago. A young woman stepped out of the line and began singing along.

A. Exercising Your Skill

The passage above takes place during a specific historical period. Historical fiction stories tell about real or imaginary characters located in actual historical settings or taking part in real historical events. Sometimes a story states a period directly. At other times, details are given that suggest or portray the time or the event.

Play an association game with a partner. One partner should read the historical detail clues below. The other partner should say what time period or event the detail *most likely* refers to. Take turns reading and relating. If neither of you can figure out what period is implied, try to find out from other people or from reference books.

Historical Detail Clues:

pony express	gladiators and the Colosseum
Sputnik	panhandlers
blue and gray uniforms	the *Mayflower*
knights, armor, horses, jousts	prairie schooners
BASIC and LOGO	pharaohs, the Sphinx, and
the Model T	hieroglyphics
Johnny Appleseed	the Acropolis at Athens
the Alamo	cattle drives
Squanto	the U.S.S. *Constitution*
Robin Hood	Plymouth rock
Buffalo Bill Cody	Tyrannosaurus Rex

B. Expanding Your Skill

With a partner decide on one of the events or time periods indicated in Part A and find more details about it. Then take turns telling a fictional chain story. You tell the first part. Your partner tells the next part, and so on. Make sure that your story includes details suggesting the mood or circumstances of the time. Tell the story to the rest of the class. When you have finished, ask your audience if they got a "feel" for the time or event portrayed.

C. Exploring Language

Decide on one of the time periods or events listed below. Do research to find more details about it. Then write a diary entry of a character who might have lived at that time. Include details that give a sense of what the time was like without actually saying what it was like. If someone reads your entry, they should be able to answer questions like these, even though the information is not stated directly: *Was electric power in use at the time? What types of transportation were used then? What did people value most then—freedom, mobility, recreation, religion, or something else?*

Historical Periods or Events:

the settling of Colonial Jamestown
the first railroad to the American West
everyday life in the Early Kingdom of Ancient Egypt
Incan life at Machu Picchu
Simón Bolívar acts as "The Liberator" of South America
the Boston Tea Party
Robert Scott heads for the South Pole
the Lewis and Clark Expedition
Daniel Boone helps open the Wilderness Road

D. Expressing Yourself

Choose one of these activities.

1. Illustrate a scene of daily life in a specific historical time period. Include details that suggest the time period and what life was like then on a daily basis. You may write a caption for your illustration, but do not be specific about the period. See if your classmates can guess the time period represented. Talk about what daily life must have been like then.

2. With two or three classmates act out a scene from a well-known historical event. Use words, body movements, and facial expressions to tell about what is happening, but do not use any words that directly name the characters or the event. See how quickly your classmates can guess the event you are acting out.